Introduction

Problems, Problems, Problems, Volume 6 is the sixth in a series of Problems Books compiled by the Canadian Mathematics Competition. The aim of the series is to provide a resource that makes it possible for all students, from senior elementary through senior secondary school levels, to experience the satisfaction of problem solving.

The focus in this volume is on topics that parallel the senior elementary and junior secondary school mathematics curriculum. The book is a companion to Volume 4 and, as a set, the two books provide the quantity and variety of problems which are essential to the development of problem solving ability.

The questions have been selected from previous Gauss and Pascal Contests. These contests are created and administered nationally, in both French and English, by the Canadian Mathematics Competition. The Gauss Contest, for grades 7 and 8, was started on a local basis by the Grand Valley Mathematics Association in the early 1970s, and is now written annually by more than 60 000 students nationwide.

The questions on the contests are all in multiple choice format. For this book, approximately one half of the questions in each section have been converted to full solution format. The questions have been organized by topic and ordered from easier to harder within each topic. Solutions to all problems are provided, but readers are urged not to give in to the temptation this provides, and to work at problems over a period of time before checking the solutions.

The organization of the book facilitates use of the problems in day-to-day classroom activity as well as for contest preparation.

We wish to thank those who assisted in the production of this book. Many teachers, (elementary, secondary, and university) have worked on the committees that produced the problems. The members of the Canadian Mathematics Competition Executive: Ed Anderson, Lloyd Auckland, Ruth Bradford, Larry Davidson, Ron Dunkley, Barry Ferguson, and Ron Scoins prepared the manuscript. We extend particular thanks to Bonnie Findlay for her excellent typesetting of the manuscript, including all diagrams. We also acknowledge the generous support of the University of Waterloo and our corporate sponsors.

The organizers of the Canadian Mathematics Competition applaud the many teachers who, through their interest and encouragement, develop a desire among their students for enrichment in mathematics. We hope that this latest problems book will provide further opportunities for students and teachers to experience the joy of mathematics.

Canadian Mathematics Competition
Faculty of Mathematics
University of Waterloo
Waterloo, Ontario, Canada
February, 1993

Canadian Mathematics Competition

PROBLEMS PROBLEMS PROBLEMS

VOLUME 6

Canadian Mathematics Competition
Faculty of Mathematics
University of Waterloo
Waterloo, Ontario, Canada
1993

Published by
Waterloo Mathematics Foundation
University of Waterloo
Waterloo, Ontario, Canada
N2L 3G1

Telephone: (519) 885-1211, extension 3030
Fax: (519) 746-6592

Canadian Cataloguing in Publication Data

Main entry under title:

Problems, problems, problems

"Canadian Mathematics Competition".
For use in high schools.
ISBN 0-921418-07-8 (v. 6)

1. Mathematics--Examinations, questions, etc.
I. Waterloo Mathematics Foundation. II. Canadian
Mathematics Competition.

QA139.P76 1988 510'.76 C88-090190-X

Printed by Graphic Services, University of Waterloo

Contents

Contest References

Each question in the book has been given a reference number of the form "year-contest-question number". For example, 1988-G8-24 indicates question 24 from the 1988 Grade 8 Gauss Contest. The contest abbreviations are: G7 - Grade 7 Gauss Contest, G8 - Grade 8 Gauss Contest, G - Gauss Contest (prior to 1985, students in Grades 7 and 8 wrote the same paper), P - Grade 9 Pascal Contest, C - Grade 10 Cayley Contest and J - Junior (prior to 1981, the Pascal, Cayley and Fermat Contests were combined into one paper called the Junior Mathematics Contest).

Questions

A sign painter is to centre a 12-letter word on a 15-foot signboard. If each letter is to be three-fifths of a foot wide and if there is to be one-fifth of a foot between consecutive letters, determine the number of feet left at each end of the board.

Fractions

Multiple Choice Questions

1991-G7-2

1. The value of $4 + \frac{2}{10} + \frac{4}{1000}$ is

   (A) 4.24 (B) 4.024 (C) 4.204 (D) 4.0024 (E) 4.2004

1984-G-1

2. The number added to $\frac{1}{2}$ to give $\frac{5}{8}$ is

   (A) $\frac{1}{8}$ (B) $\frac{4}{6}$ (C) $\frac{6}{10}$ (D) $\frac{9}{8}$ (E) none of these

1992-G8-4

3. The value of $\frac{1}{2}+\frac{1}{3}+\frac{1}{4}+\frac{2}{3}+\frac{2}{4}+\frac{3}{4}$ is

(A) 3 (B) 2 (C) $3\frac{1}{12}$ (D) $\frac{1}{2}$ (E) $2\frac{5}{6}$

1984-P-3

4. $1\frac{1}{3}\times 1\frac{1}{2}$ is equal to

(A) $1\frac{1}{6}$ (B) $2\frac{1}{6}$ (C) 2 (D) $2\frac{5}{6}$ (E) $1\frac{5}{6}$

1987-P-4

5. If $a=2$ and $b=3$, then $\frac{1}{a}+\frac{1}{b}$ equals

(A) $\frac{1}{5}$ (B) 1 (C) 5 (D) $\frac{2}{5}$ (E) $\frac{5}{6}$

1975-G-1

6. The value of $\frac{3}{4}+\frac{5}{2}\times\frac{3}{4}$ is

(A) $\frac{39}{16}$ (B) $\frac{21}{8}$ (C) 1 (D) $\frac{3}{2}$ (E) $\frac{39}{4}$

1983-P-1

7. You are given one hour to complete a contest. The fraction of the hour remaining for you to complete the contest after thirty-five minutes have elapsed is

(A) 25 (B) $\frac{1}{4}$ (C) $\frac{7}{20}$ (D) $\frac{7}{12}$ (E) $\frac{5}{12}$

1987-G7-5

8. An expression equal to $\frac{7}{12}$ is

(A) $\frac{7}{3}+\frac{1}{4}$ (B) $\frac{7}{9}+\frac{7}{3}$ (C) $\frac{4}{7}+\frac{3}{5}$ (D) $\frac{1}{4}+\frac{1}{3}$ (E) $\frac{1}{2}+\frac{1}{6}$

1990-P-6

9. It requires 9 hours to fill $\frac{3}{5}$ of a swimming pool. At this rate, the number of hours required to fill the remainder of the pool is

(A) $\frac{2}{5}$ (B) $3\frac{3}{5}$ (C) $5\frac{2}{5}$ (D) 6 (E) 15

1986-G8-4

10. The value of $\left(3\frac{1}{3}\right)^2$ is

(A) $11\frac{1}{9}$ (B) $9\frac{1}{9}$ (C) $6\frac{2}{3}$ (D) $\frac{100}{3}$ (E) $\frac{101}{9}$

1976-G-9

11. The value of $\frac{1}{3} + \frac{2}{5} \div \frac{8}{3}$ is

(A) $\frac{11}{40}$ (B) $\frac{88}{45}$ (C) $\frac{29}{60}$ (D) $\frac{4}{23}$ (E) $\frac{21}{20}$

1986-C-8

12. The value of $2 + \cfrac{2}{2 + \cfrac{2}{2+2}}$ is

(A) 3 (B) 7 (C) $2\frac{2}{5}$ (D) $2\frac{2}{3}$ (E) $2\frac{4}{5}$

1977-G-6

13. If $a = 3$ and $b = -1$, the value of $\frac{(a+b)^3}{(a-b)^2}$ is

(A) $\frac{1}{2}$ (B) $-\frac{1}{16}$ (C) 1 (D) 8 (E) 2

1989-P-9

14. If the value of $\frac{n}{40}$ lies between $\frac{1}{5}$ and $\frac{1}{4}$, then a possible value of n is

(A) 10 (B) 9 (C) 8 (D) 7 (E) 6

1967-J-8

15. A sign painter is to centre a 12-letter word on a 15-foot signboard. If each letter is to be three-fifths of a foot wide and if there is to be one-fifth of a foot between consecutive letters, then the number of feet left at each end of the board will be

(A) $\frac{27}{10}$ (B) $\frac{28}{5}$ (C) $\frac{27}{5}$ (D) $\frac{14}{5}$ (E) none of these

1982-P-14

16. A ball bounces $\frac{2}{3}$ of the distance through which it falls. If the second rebound is 72 cm, the height, in cm, through which the ball originally dropped was

(A) 162 (B) 32 (C) 108 (D) 48 (E) none of these

Full Solution Questions

1992-G7-2

1. Determine the decimal representation of $1 + \frac{3}{10} + \frac{41}{100}$.

1979-G-2

2. Evaluate the sum $1\frac{1}{2} + 2\frac{2}{3}$.

1980-G-5

3. Find the fraction equivalent to $1 + \frac{1}{1 + \frac{1}{2}}$.

1983-G-7

4. The sum of two fractions is $\frac{11}{12}$. If one fraction is $\frac{1}{4}$, what is the second fraction?

1987-G7-8

5. What is the sum of $\frac{1}{3}$ and half of $\frac{1}{3}$?

1982-P-9

6. In a class of 30 students, 12 are boys. If 6 more girls join the class, what fraction of the class is now female?

1982-P-8

7. A pole is painted in white, green, and blue sections. If one-third of the pole is white and one-quarter of the pole is green, then what fraction of the pole is blue?

1989-G8-3

8. At what time would a $2\frac{1}{2}$ hour test finish if it started at 9:47?

1977-G-7

9. Determine the value of $\frac{2}{3} \div \frac{2}{9} + \frac{1}{2}$.

1989-P-11

10. If $\frac{5}{6}$ of a number is 60, what is $\frac{3}{4}$ of the original number?

1984-G-13

11. What is the value of the product $\left(1 - \frac{1}{2}\right)\left(1 - \frac{1}{3}\right)\left(1 - \frac{1}{4}\right)\left(1 - \frac{1}{5}\right)$?

1981-G-14

12. Determine which of the fractions $\frac{3}{8}$, $\frac{4}{5}$, $\frac{31}{40}$, $\frac{9}{20}$, and $\frac{7}{10}$ is greater than $\frac{1}{2}$ and less than $\frac{3}{4}$.

1978-G-4

13. Determine the value of $\frac{x - y}{x + y}$ when $x = \frac{3}{4}$ and $y = \frac{2}{3}$.

1986-P-15

14. If $\frac{1}{3} + \frac{1}{4} + \frac{1}{n} = 1$, determine the value of n.

1987-C-13

15. It takes $4\frac{1}{2}$ minutes to play Billy's favourite song on a disc recorded at 45 r.p.m. (revolutions per minute). Billy accidentally played this disc at $33\frac{1}{3}$ r.p.m. How many revolutions of the disc were required to play the song?

1981-J-19

16. What is the minimum number of identical square tiles required to completely tile a rectangle having dimensions $3\frac{3}{5}$ units by $4\frac{1}{5}$ units?

The diagram shows part of the scale of a measuring device. What reading is indicated by the arrow?

Estimation and Ordering

Multiple Choice Questions

1979-G-9

1. Which of the following is false?

   (A) $(-2)(-3) \geq -9$ (B) $(-2)(-3) \leq 10$ (C) $(-2)(-3) > 0$

   (D) $(-2)(-3) = 6$ (E) $(-2)(-3) = -6$

1987-G7-3

2. Of the given values, 299×301 is closest to

   (A) 60000 (B) 90000 (C) 6000 (D) 50000 (E) 9000

1977-G-3

3. An integer which is smaller than –3 is

(A) –2 (B) $-\frac{35}{12}$ (C) $-\frac{7}{2}$ (D) –25 (E) –3.1

1988-G7-2

4. If $m = 1$ and $n = 5$, the expression which has the greatest value is

(A) $m + n$ (B) $\frac{m}{n}$ (C) $n - m$ (D) $m \times n$ (E) $m - n$

1985-G7-17

5. The value of $\frac{789 \times 97}{0.04}$ is closest to

(A) 200 (B) 2000 (C) 20 000 (D) 2 000 000 (E) 20 000 000

1986-G7-8

6. Jill uses an average of 20 L of gas per week. She pays 48¢ per litre. Of the following, the closest estimate of her yearly gas bill, in dollars, is

(A) 100 (B) 300 (C) 500 (D) 600 (E) 1000

1985-F-10

7. Of the following, the best approximation for $\sqrt[3]{\frac{6.01}{0.099} + 3.95}$ is

(A) 4 (B) 8 (C) 9 (D) 25 (E) 3

1990-G7-10

8. The approximate number of seconds in one year is

(A) 30 000 000 (B) 3 000 000 (C) 1 500 000 (D) 500 000 (E) 80 000

1991-G7-9

9. The area of the country called SSUAG is 850 000 km^2. Two hundred million people live there. Of the answers given, the best approximation of the number of people per square kilometre is

(A) 0.004 (B) 20 (C) 400 (D) 200 (E) 2000

1984-C-17

10. If $x - y > x$ and $y - x < y$, then

(A) $x < 0$ (B) $x < y$ (C) $x = y$ (D) $y > 0$ (E) $x > y$

1977-J-7

11. If $\frac{1}{a} + \frac{1}{b} = \frac{1}{c}$, and if $a = 2$ and $b = 3$, then c is

(A) between 0 and 1 (B) 1 (C) between 1 and 2
(D) between 2 and 4 (E) greater than 4

1986-G7-12

12. Whenever Sandy enters a two-digit number into his calculator, he always enters the digits in reverse order. When asked to add up the numbers 89, 98, 47, 77, and 85, his answer would be
(A) too big by 72 (B) too small by 72 (C) too big by 36
(D) too small by 36 (E) correct

1981-J-9

13. If x, y, and z are positive numbers and $3x = 5y = 2z$, then
(A) $x < y < z$ (B) $y < x < z$ (C) $y < z < x$ (D) $z < y < x$ (E) $x < z < y$

1964-J-9

14. If y is a negative integer, which of the following has the greatest value?
(A) $\frac{13}{24}y$ (B) $\frac{12}{24}y$ (C) $\frac{11}{24}y$ (D) $\frac{11}{21}y$ (E) $\frac{11}{20}y$

1965-J-5

15. If $x > y > 0$ and $z \neq 0$, the inequality which is not always correct is
(A) $xz > yz$ (B) $x - z > y - z$ (C) $x + z > y + z$
(D) $\frac{x}{z^2} > \frac{y}{z^2}$ (E) $xz^2 > yz^2$

Full Solution Questions

1987-G8-2

1. Arrange the numbers -5.5, 0, -0.5 in order from least to greatest.

1988-G7-1

2. When the numbers 5.02, 5.18, 5.2, 5.007, and 5.018 are arranged from least to greatest, determine the middle number.

1982-G-4

3. Find the integer closest to $\frac{14}{3} - \frac{2}{5} \times \frac{11}{6}$.

1991-G8-3

4. Find the third greatest value in the set $\left\{\frac{1}{8}, 0.8, -8, \frac{-1}{8}, 1^8\right\}$.

1979-G-13

5. Find the sum of the smallest and largest numbers from the set $\left\{-4, -11, \frac{1}{2}, 2, -7\right\}$.

1979-G-11

6. If $d = 4$, find the smallest number in the set $\left\{2d, -d, -\frac{1}{2}d, \frac{16}{d}, \frac{0}{d}\right\}$.

1981-G-7

7. If $d = -5$, find the smallest number in the set $\left\{-3d, 2d, \frac{15}{d}, d^2, \frac{0}{d}\right\}$.

1992-G8-2

8. The diagram shows part of the scale of a measuring device. What reading is indicated by the arrow?

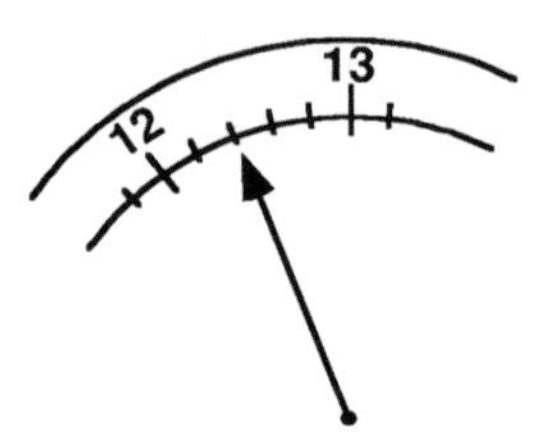

1988-G8-7

9. If n is an integer, then $n + 3$, $n + 9$, $n - 4$, $n + 6$, and $n - 1$ are also integers. When these five integers are arranged from least to greatest, which one is in the middle?

1982-G-19

10. Which of the numbers -20, $-\frac{3}{4}$, 0, $\frac{1}{2}$, and 10 is greater than its square?

1984-C-12

11. The positive integers are written consecutively in groups of five so that the first row contains 1, 2, 3, 4, 5, the second row 6, 7, 8, 9, 10, etc. Find the row which has a sum nearest to the value of 150.

1966-J-6

12. If x has a value between 4 and 8, and y has a value between 20 and 40, find the maximum and minimum values for $\frac{y}{x}$.

1991-G8-23

13. If $0 < x < 1$ and y is a positive integer, find the largest value in the set $\left\{\frac{x}{y}, \frac{y}{x}, x^y, y - x, xy\right\}$.

Area and Perimeter

Multiple Choice Questions

1980-G-4

1. The perimeter of the given figure is

   (A) 36 cm (B) 44 cm (C) 52 cm
   (D) 60 cm (E) 72 cm

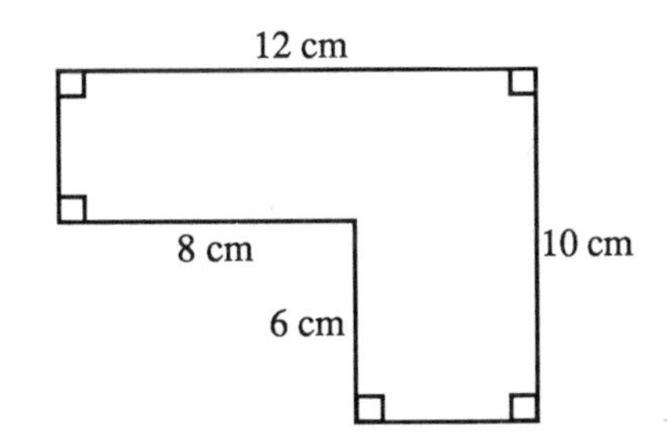

1974-G-5

2. In the diagram, $AD = 4$ cm, $BC = 5$ cm, and $AB = 4\frac{1}{2}$ cm. The area of triangle ABC, in square cm, is
(A) 20 (B) 9 (C) $11\frac{1}{4}$
(D) $22\frac{1}{2}$ (E) 10

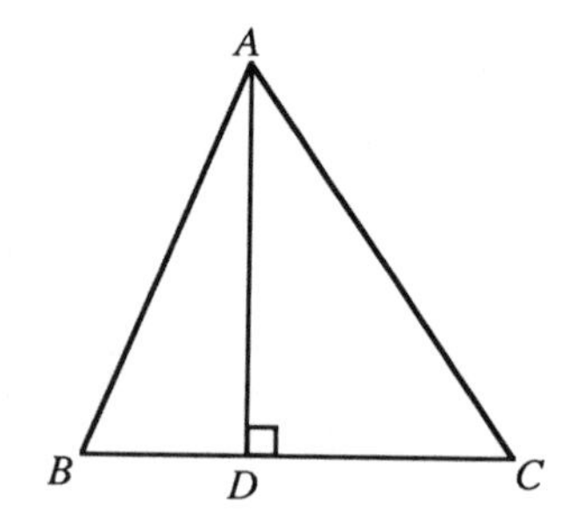

1979-G-5

3. In rectangle $ABCD$, $AD = 12$ cm and the area is 60 cm². The length, in cm, of AB is
(A) 5 (B) 10 (C) 12
(D) 13 (E) 60

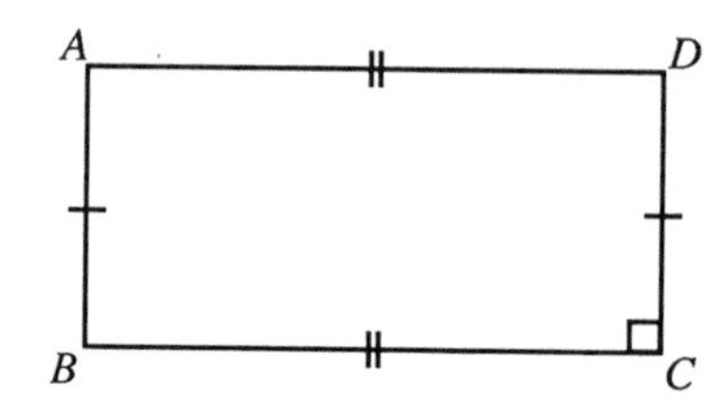

1992-G8-7

4. Of the five figures shown, the one with the greatest perimeter is
(A) A (B) B (C) C
(D) D (E) E

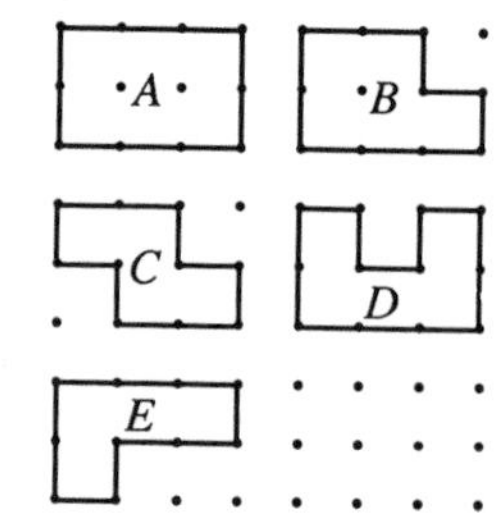

1974-G-11

5. The area of the shaded part of the square is
(A) $4x + 2y$ (B) $(x + y)^2$ (C) $(x + y)y - x^2$
(D) $y^2 - x^2$ (E) $x^2 - y^2$

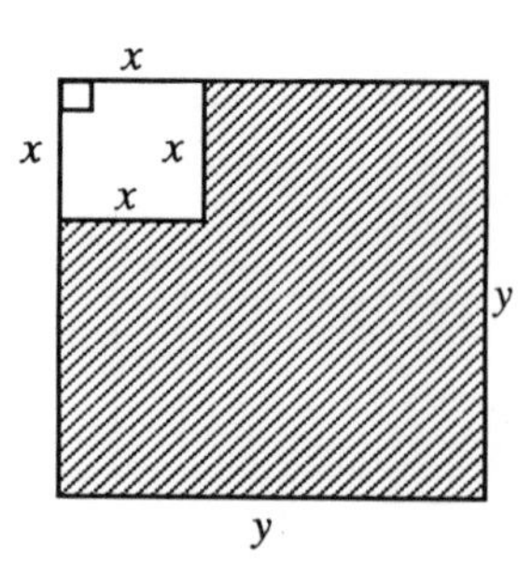

1976-G-8

6. In the diagram, the rectangle has length 11 and width 7. The area of the shaded part is

(A) $\frac{77}{2}$ (B) 37.5 (C) 72
(D) $\frac{67}{2}$ (E) $\frac{231}{4}$

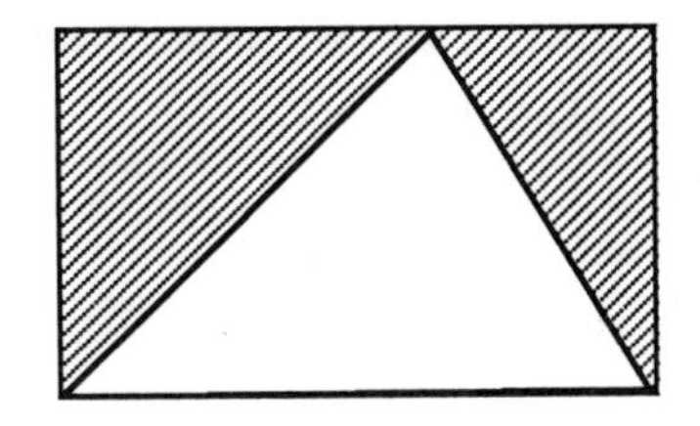

1987-G7-6

7. If the length of each line segment in the figure is 2 cm, the area of the figure, in cm^2, will be

(A) 24 (B) 16 (C) 20
(D) 30 (E) 36

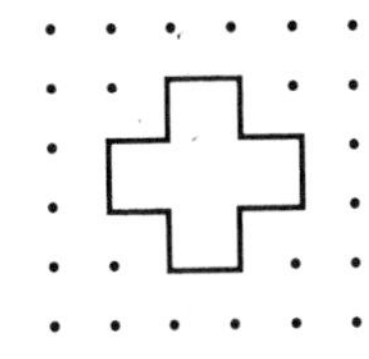

1983-G-12

8. In the diagram, rectangle $ABCD$ has length 10 cm and height 8 cm; triangle ADE has height 4 cm. The area of the shaded part, in cm^2, is

(A) 20 (B) 40 (C) 60
(D) 80 (E) 100

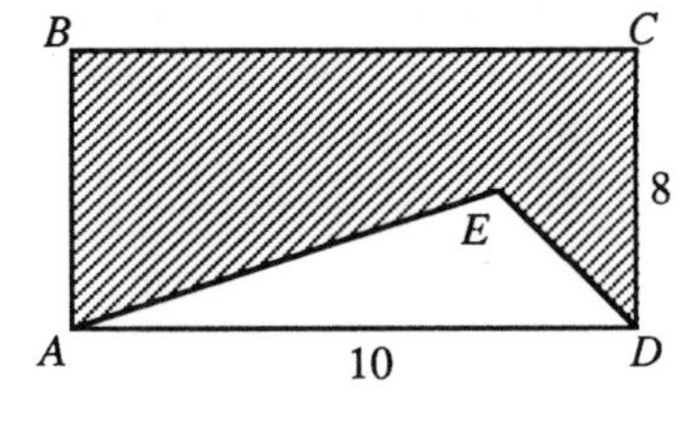

1982-G-13

9. The area of figure $ABCD$, in m^2, is

(A) 48 (B) 138 (C) 168
(D) 108 (E) 173

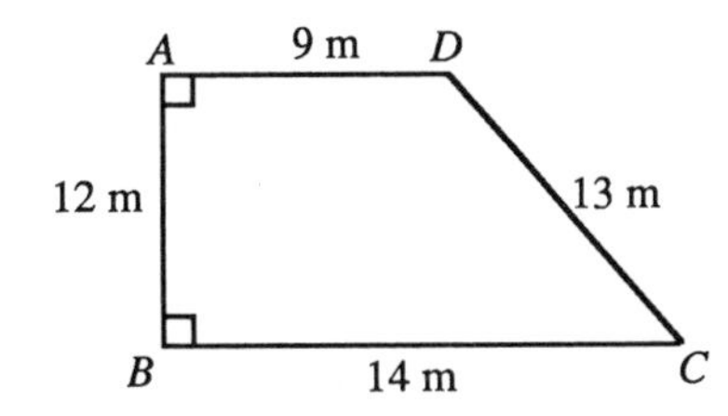

1977-G-13

10. A garden, 10 m × 20 m, is enclosed by a sidewalk of width 1 m. The area of the sidewalk, in square metres, is

(A) 231 (B) 31 (C) 264 (D) 64 (E) none of these

1976-G-17

11. The areas of the two squares inside square $ABCD$ are 4 cm^2 and 9 cm^2. The area of the shaded part, in cm^2, is
    (A) 13 (B) 12 (C) 36
    (D) 6 (E) 72

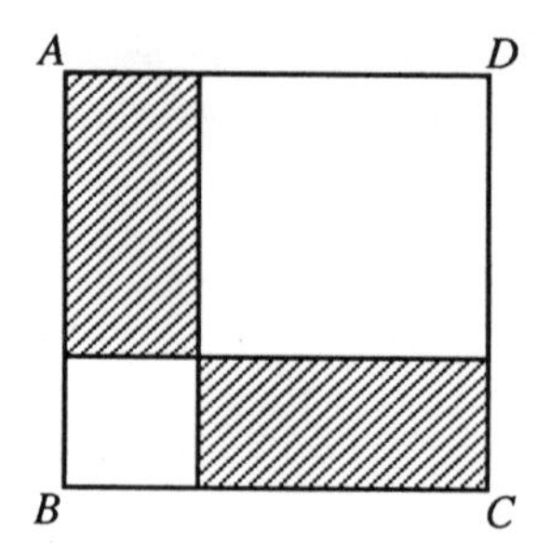

1991-G7-15

12. An isosceles triangle has sides that measure 10 cm and 3 cm. The perimeter of the triangle, in centimetres, is
    (A) 30 (B) 26 (C) 23 (D) 16 (E) 13

1978-G-19

13. In rectangle $ABCD$, $AD = 8$ and $AB = 6$. The total area of the shaded parts is
    (A) 28 (B) 17 (C) 10
    (D) 14 (E) 24

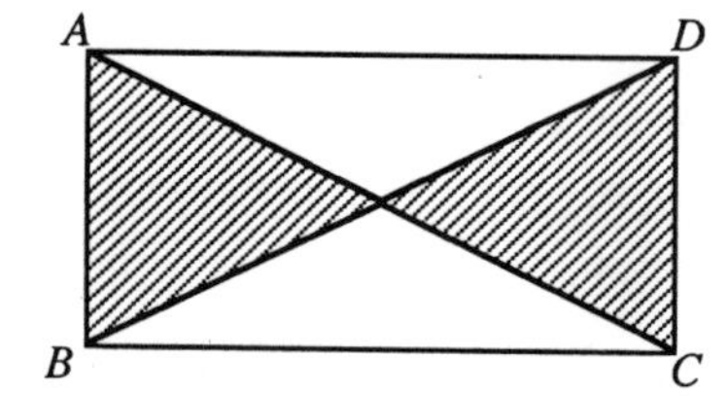

1991-G8-18

14. In rectangle $ABCD$, the side AB is twice the length of AD, $AF = FB = DG = GC$, and E is the midpoint of AD. The ratio of the shaded area to the area of $ABCD$ is
    (A) $\frac{1}{3}$ (B) $\frac{1}{4}$ (C) $\frac{3}{4}$
    (D) $\frac{5}{8}$ (E) $\frac{3}{8}$

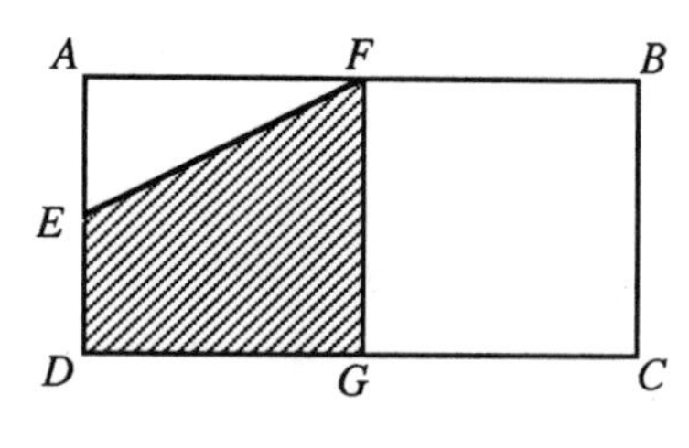

1977-G-22

15. Two squares have sides of lengths x cm and $(2x + 1)$ cm, respectively. The sum of the perimeters of the two squares equals 100 cm. The length of each side of the larger square, in cm, is
    (A) 8 (B) 17 (C) 12 (D) 33 (E) 65

1977-G-25

16. In ΔABC, $AD = 2$, $BC = 6$, and $AC = 4$. The length of BE is

    (A) $\frac{4}{3}$ (B) 2 (C) 3

    (D) $\frac{2}{3}$ (E) $\frac{8}{9}$

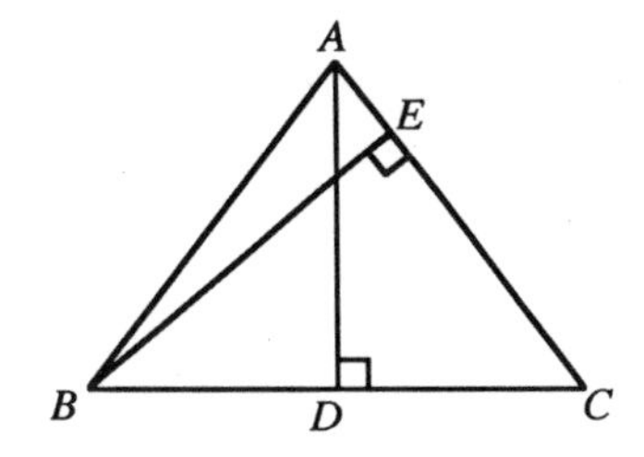

Full Solution Questions

1976-G-7

1. The length of a rectangular room is 7 feet more than its width. If the perimeter is 34 feet, find the length of the room.

1986-G7-10

2. The diagram on the right shows the floor plan of the Aardvark warehouse. Find the perimeter of the warehouse.

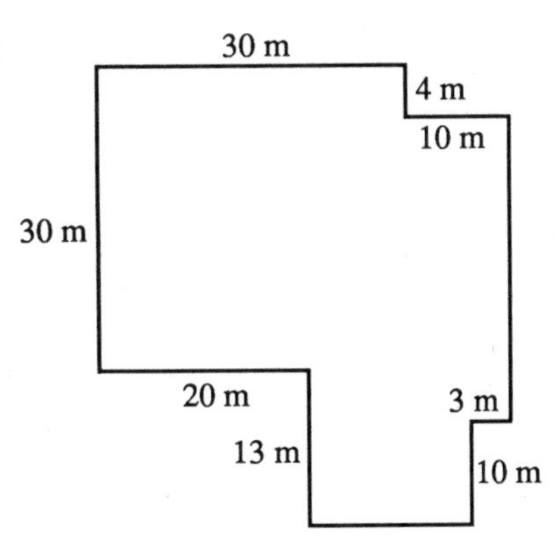

1975-G-10

3. If $AB = 4$ units, $AD = 3$ units, and $DC = 6$ units, find the area of $ABCD$.

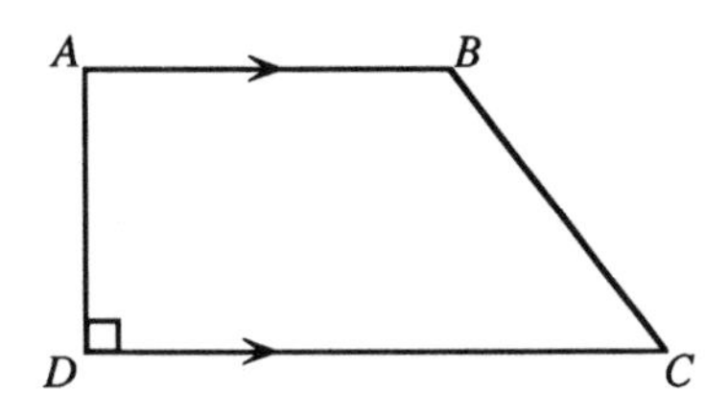

1988-G7-11

4. Each visible face of a block in the pile measures 2 cm by 8 cm. Find the length of the path marked with the solid line segments.

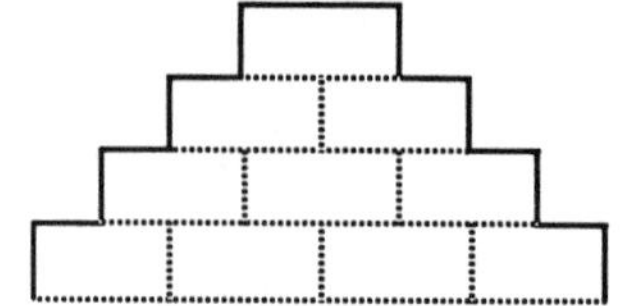

1992-G7-10

5. The given shape has a uniform width of 1 unit. The other dimensions are indicated on the diagram. Find the area of this shape.

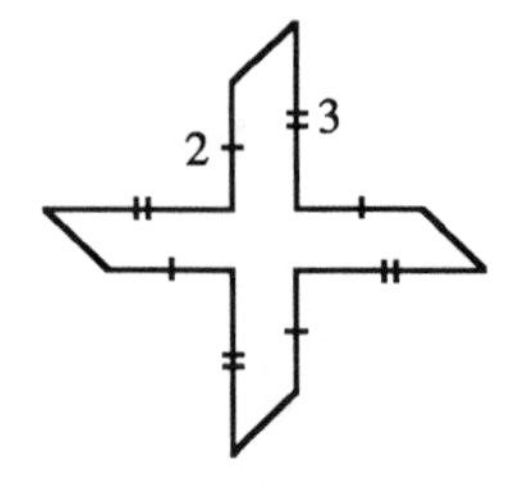

1986-G7-16

6. The perimeter of a rectangle is 64 cm and its length is 20 cm. Find the area of the rectangle.

1980-G-20

7. A circle of radius 7 cm is placed in a square of side 20 cm as in the diagram. Approximating π by $\frac{22}{7}$, find the area of the square ***not*** covered by the circle.

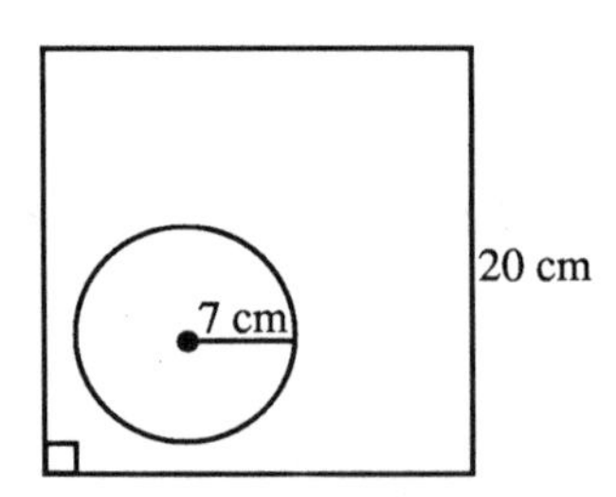

1980-G-17

8. If the area of triangle ADC is 24 square units, find the area of triangle ABD.

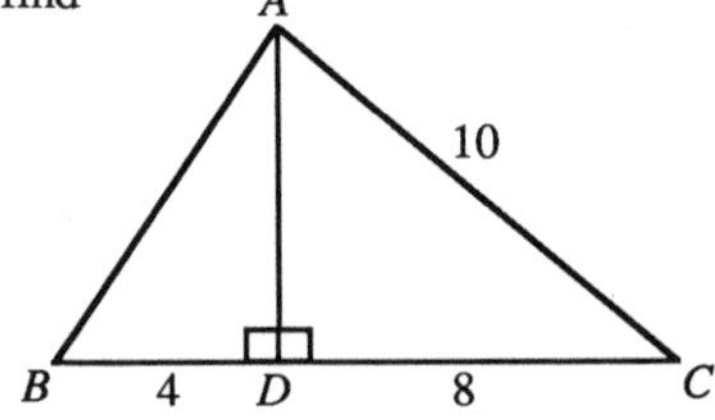

1992-G8-13

9. Two equal circles are placed in a rectangle, as shown. The distance between the centres of the circles is 8 cm. Find the area of the rectangle.

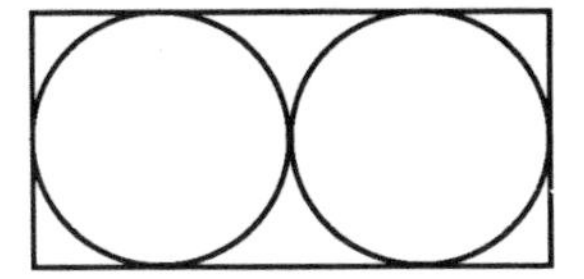

1990-G7-19

10. The length and width, in metres, of the rectangle shown are integers. The area of the shaded region is 6.5 m^2. Find the perimeter of the rectangle.

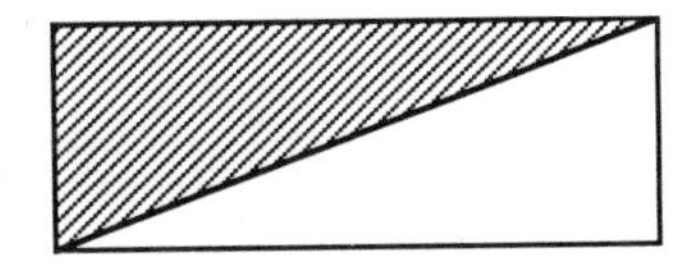

1991-G8-21

11. In the diagram, AB is parallel to DC. The semicircle AED has diameter AD of length 4 cm. Find the perimeter of the figure.

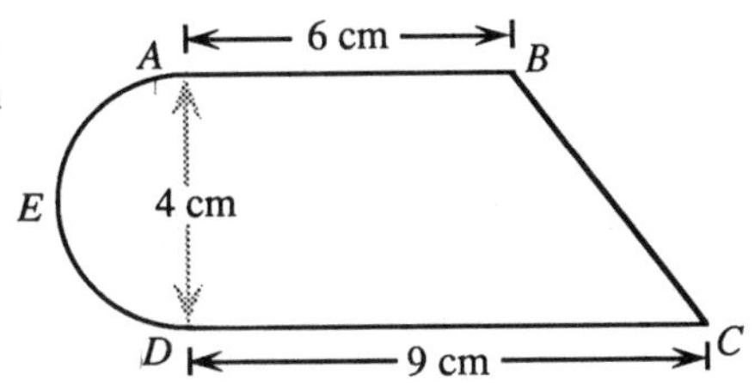

1985-G8-16

12. In ΔABC, BE and CD are altitudes. The area of ΔABC is 48 square units. CD is 6 units and BE is 8 units. Find the sum of AB and AC.

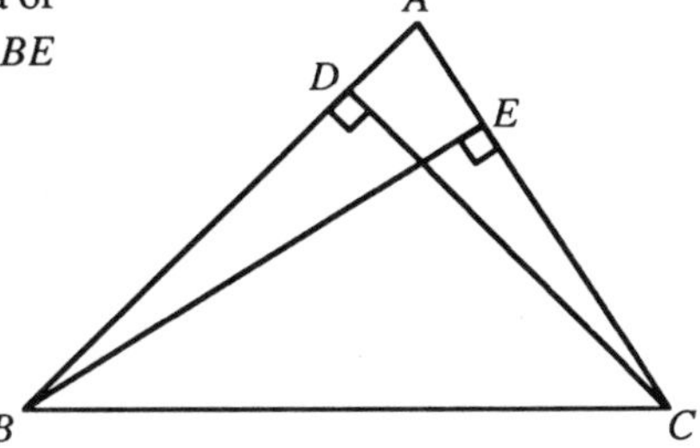

1974-G-19

13. A right-angled triangle has sides 3 inches, 4 inches, and 5 inches, and an area of 6 square inches. Find the area of a triangle whose sides are three times the lengths of the original sides.

1987-G7-23

14. Square $QRST$ and triangle PRS have the same area. Square $QRST$ has sides of length 12. Find the length of PR.

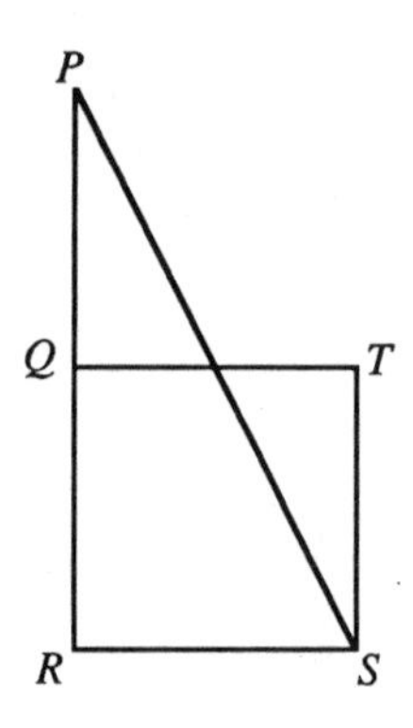

1990-G7-22

15. A square measuring 10 cm by 10 cm is cut into pieces. The pieces are rearranged to form two other squares. The lengths of the sides of these squares, in centimetres, are integers. Find the total perimeter of the two new squares.

1988-G7-23

16. The dots are one unit apart, horizontally and vertically. Find the area of the figure shown.

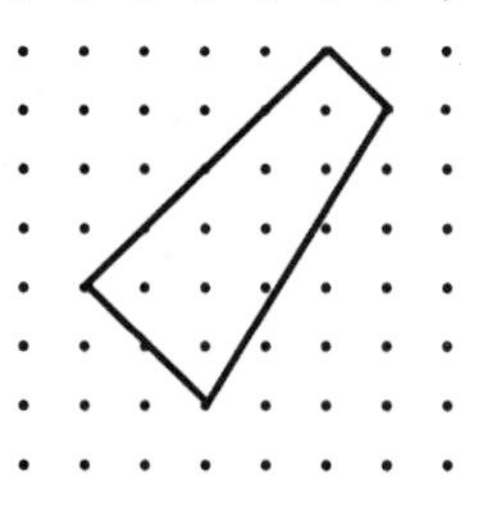

Joe Blow receives 10% off every purchase at Harry's Hardware. Unfortunately, he must pay 7% sales tax on the reduced price. How much would Joe pay for a drill whose regular price is $14.00?

Percentages - II

Multiple Choice Questions

1977-G-4

1. 20% of 20 is

   (A) $\frac{1}{5}$ (B) 40 (C) 400 (D) 1 (E) 4

1975-J-1

2. $\frac{1}{10}$ of 1% is

   (A) 10 (B) 0.1 (C) 0.01 (D) 0.001 (E) 0.0001

1983-P-6

3. To the nearest whole number, 115% of 15 is

   (A) 15 (B) 16 (C) 17 (D) 18 (E) none of these

1976-J-2

4. If 2% of a number is 8, then the number is
(A) 0.16 (B) 4 (C) 16 (D) 400 (E) 800

1975-G-3

5. On an examination, 13 students passed and 3 students failed. The failure rate, in percent, is
(A) $18\frac{3}{4}$ (B) $\frac{300}{13}$ (C) $\frac{1300}{3}$ (D) $23\frac{1}{3}$ (E) $43\frac{1}{3}$

1988-G8-5

6. In Canada, approximately 46% of the population has Type O blood. If there are 25 000 000 Canadians, the best estimate of the number with Type O blood is
(A) 12 500 000 (B) 11 500 000 (C) 1 250 000 (D) 1 150 000 (E) 115 000

1981-G-6

7. A merchant reduces the price of a $25.00 article by 35 percent. The sale price is
(A) $24.65 (B) $8.75 (C) $16.25 (D) $17.25 (E) $16.00

1974-G-12

8. A coat with an original price of $85.50 is reduced by 10%. The new selling price of the coat is
(A) $94.05 (B) $77.05 (C) $76.55 (D) $76.95 (E) $77.95

1975-J-10

9. The price of an article is reduced by 20%. In order to restore the reduced price to the original value, the reduced price must be increased by
(A) 20% (B) $22\frac{1}{2}$% (C) 25% (D) 30% (E) 15%

1985-G8-7

10. If Bob earns $25 000 a year and Frank earns 6% more than Bob, then the amount that Frank earns, in dollars, is
(A) 26 500 (B) 25 150 (C) 25 015 (D) 15 000 (E) 1 500

1979-G-17

11. In a class of 30 students, 40% wear glasses. Three of those wearing glasses are left-handed. Of those wearing glasses, the percent who are left-handed is
(A) 10 (B) 25 (C) $7\frac{1}{2}$ (D) 3 (E) 4

1992-F-10

12. During the basketball season, Pierre scored 25% more points than Jim. Pierre scored 220 points for the season. The number of points Jim scored was
(A) 245 (B) 195 (C) 166 (D) 176 (E) 274

1991-P-15

13. In a recent election with three candidates, Mrs. Jones received 10 575 votes, Mr. Smith received 7990 votes, and Mr. Green received 2585 votes. If 90% of those eligible to vote did so, the number of eligible voters was
(A) 19 035 (B) 49 572 (C) 23 265 (D) 21 150 (E) 23 500

1992-G7-9

14. A teacher purchased twenty Gauss Contest Problems Books costing $10.00 each. The only tax she paid on the books was the 7% Goods and Services Tax (GST). The cost of the books, including GST, in dollars, was
(A) 270.00 (B) 214.00 (C) 340.00 (D) 201.40 (E) 200.70

1987-G7-16

15. Expressed as a percent, $0.33 \div 0.11$ is
(A) 3 (B) 30 (C) 0.3 (D) 300 (E) $33\frac{1}{3}$

1963-J-25

16. Mr. Jones sold two pipes at $1.20 each. Based on the cost, the profit on one was 20% and the loss on the other was 20%. On the sale of the pipes he
(A) broke even (B) lost 4 cents (C) gained 4 cents
(D) lost 10 cents (E) gained 10 cents

Full Solution Questions

1978-G-5

1. Find $\frac{2}{3}$% of 600.

1972-J-2

2. What is the value of 20 increased by 200% of itself?

1982-G-2

3. An item is on sale for 30% off the regular price of $7.00. What is the sale price?

1976-G-5

4. Joe Blow receives 10% off every purchase at Harry's Hardware. Unfortunately, he must pay 7% sales tax on the reduced price. How much would Joe pay for a drill whose regular price is $14.00?

1964-J-2

5. A baseball team has won 50 games out of 75 played and has 45 games still to play. How many of the remaining games must it win in order that its percentage of games won for the entire season will be 60%?

1978-G-12

6. The selling price of a coat, which normally sells for $55.00, was reduced by 20% during the spring sale. Since the coat still didn't sell, the sale price was reduced by 10%. What was the total reduction from the original price?

1990-P-9

7. If x is 3% of y and y is 7% of w, find x in terms of w.

1990-G7-8

8. In 1987, the price of one kilogram of Schwartz' cheese was $12.00. In 1988, the price was increased by 10%. In 1989, the 1988 price was increased by 10%. What was the price of one kilogram of cheese in 1989?

1986-G8-18

9. Suppose the value of one American dollar is 30% more than the value of one Canadian dollar. An American tourist in Canada purchases a $35.00 souvenir with thirty American dollars. What should his change, in Canadian dollars, be from this purchase?

1977-G-16

10. An article which normally sells for $16.00 is on sale at 30% off. If you bought this article at the sale price, what is the amount you would pay, including 7% sales tax?

1987-G8-15

11. A $100 article is reduced by 20% for a sale. In order to restore the price to $100, what is the percentage by which the sale price must be increased?

1976-J-13

12. The length of a rectangle is increased by 15% and the width is decreased by 20%. Find the percentage change in the area of the rectangle.

1990-C-12

13. Some companies pay bonuses for increased daily production. Cayley Industries pays a worker 70 cents per unit for the first 50 units produced, 80 cents per unit for the next 30 units produced, and 90 cents per unit for the remaining units. What is the number of units produced by a worker who earned $86 in a day?

1977-J-8

14. A baseball team has won 50% of the 60 games it has played. Find the number of games the team must win in succession to increase its winning percentage to 60%.

1992-P-15

15. In a recent survey, 40% of the cars contained two or more people. Of those cars containing only one person, 25% contained a male. Find the percentage of all cars which contained exactly one female and no male.

An uptown bus leaves the terminal every 45 minutes and a downtown bus leaves the same terminal every 54 minutes. If an uptown bus and a downtown bus both leave the terminal at 1400 hours, find the next time the two buses leave together.

Divisibility and Factoring

Multiple Choice Questions

1978-G-8

1. The difference between the L.C.M. and H.C.F. of the numbers 5, 10, and 35 is
   (A) 65 (B) 1745 (C) 35 (D) 5 (E) 30

1976-G-25

2. The number of divisors of 105, other than 1 and 105, is
   (A) 5 (B) 6 (C) 7 (D) 8 (E) 9

1979-G-24

3. $2^{10} - 1$ is divisible by
   (A) 2 (B) 10 (C) 3 (D) 4 (E) 8

1978-G-25

4. $2^7 - 2$ is divided by 7 and $2^5 - 2$ is divided by 5. The sum of the quotients is
(A) 0 (B) 23 (C) 24 (D) $48\frac{24}{35}$ (E) $24\frac{24}{35}$

1987-P-9

5. A number which is a multiple of 15, but not a multiple of 18, is
(A) 180 (B) 320 (C) 360 (D) 420 (E) 540

1992-G7-12

6. The three brass numbers 1, 2, and 3 can be used to form a three-digit house number such as 231. The number of these three-digit house numbers that are divisible by 6 is
(A) 2 (B) 1 (C) 6 (D) 4 (E) 0

1980-G-21

7. $N = 20\times19\times18\times17\times16\times15\times14\times13\times12\times11\times10\times9\times8\times7\times6\times5\times4\times3\times2\times1$.
Of the following five numbers, the largest one that divides N exactly is
(A) 9 000 000 (B) 900 000 (C) 90 000 (D) 9000 (E) 900

1975-G-17

8. The smallest value of K so that $60K$ is a perfect square is
(A) 60 (B) 15 (C) 6 (D) 45 (E) 9

1975-G-26

9. A perfect number is a number which equals the sum of its proper divisors. For example, 6 is perfect since $6 = 1 + 2 + 3$. The next perfect number is
(A) 28 (B) 16 (C) 24 (D) 8 (E) 36

1985-G7-21

10. The interior of circle A contains only the positive integers from 1 to 50. Circle B contains only the odd numbers from 1 to 50. Circle C contains only the multiples of 7 from 1 to 50. The number of numbers in the shaded area is
(A) 7 (B) 5 (C) 4
(D) 3 (E) 1

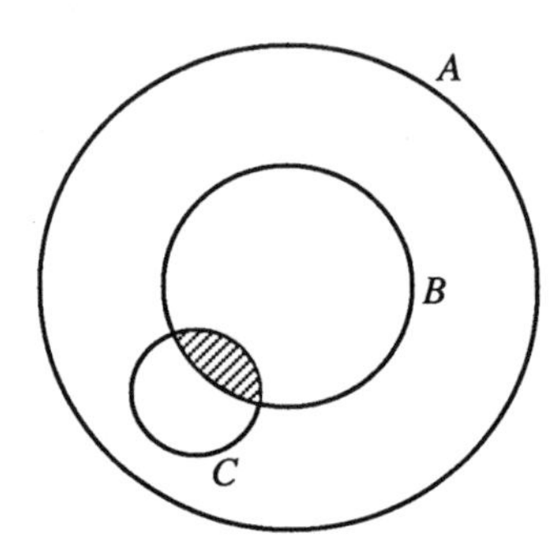

1966-J-22

11. The least positive integer having the remainders 1, 4, and 1 when divided by 3, 5, and 11, respectively, lies between

    (A) 11 and 20 (B) 21 and 30 (C) 31 and 40 (D) 41 and 50 (E) 61 and 70

1981-G-26

12. If n is a positive integer, an integer which is always divisible by 3 is

    (A) $(n+1)(n+4)$ (B) $n(n+2)(n+6)$ (C) $n(n+2)(n+4)$
    (D) $n(n+3)(n-3)$ (E) $(n+2)(n+3)(n+5)$

1990-G8-13

13. Two gear wheels, A and B, are in contact. Wheel A has 35 teeth. Wheel B has 21 teeth. The least number of revolutions wheel B must turn before the two wheels return to their starting positions is

    (A) 3 (B) 5 (C) 7
    (D) 21 (E) 28

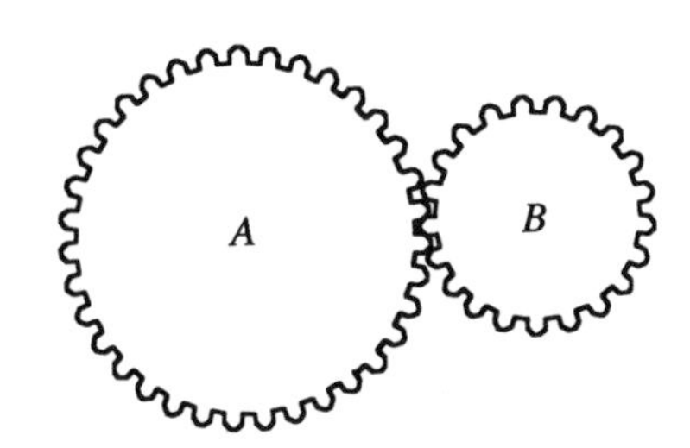

1989-G7-20

14. Every 12 minutes a bus leaves from Walperville for Georgetown. Every 20 minutes a bus leaves from Walperville for Burnt River. Buses leave at 1:00 p.m. for both places. Another time when buses will be leaving for both places is

    (A) 1:32 p.m. (B) 2:20 p.m. (C) 2:40 p.m. (D) 3:00 p.m. (E) 3:40 p.m.

Full Solution Questions

1977-G-9

1. Find the highest common factor of 12, 20, and 36.

1974-G-10

2. Find the sum of the H.C.F. and L.C.M. of the numbers 4, 20, and 28.

1979-G-19

3. Find the sum of the divisors of 24, including 1 and 24.

1976-G-15

4. Find the set of all prime numbers greater than 6 and less than 37.

1988-G8-4

5. If $45 \times 45 \times N = 90 \times 90 \times 90$, find the value of N.

1981-G-20

6. Find the smallest positive integer N so that $120 \times N$ will be a perfect square.

1977-G-24

7. Find the smallest integer n which will make $12n$ divisible by 28.

1987-G7-18

8. Given that $12\,345\,679 \times 9 = 111\,111\,111$, and n is a number such that $12\,345\,679 \times n = 666\,666\,666$, find the value of n.

1988-G7-13

9. Erin's age, when divided by 2, 3, 4, 5, or 6 gives a remainder of 1. Find the least age that Erin could be given that she is older than 1.

1980-G-23

10. An uptown bus leaves the terminal every 45 minutes and a downtown bus leaves the same terminal every 54 minutes. If an uptown bus and a downtown bus both leave the terminal at 1400 hours, find the next time the two buses leave together.

1976-G-22

11. A bell rings every 42 minutes, and a buzzer sounds every 36 minutes. If they sound together at 9:00 a.m., find the time they next will sound together.

1980-G-11

12. A small gear makes 32 revolutions per minute. A larger gear connected to the smaller gear makes 20 revolutions per minute. Find the number of revolutions the larger gear has made when the smaller gear has made 36 revolutions.

1964-J-11

13. A six-digit number is formed by repeating a three-digit number; for example, 265 265 or 345 345. What is the largest integer which will divide all such numbers?

1988-C-19

14. The digits 1, 2, 3, 4, and 5 are each used once to compose a five-digit number *abcde*, such that the three-digit number *abc* is divisible by 4, *bcd* is divisible by 5, and *cde* is divisible by 3. Find the number *abcde*.

A small foreign car uses 12 litres of gas to make a 144 km trip. How many litres of gas are required by this car to travel 336 km?

Number Sentences and Word Problems

Multiple Choice Questions

1981-G-4

1. A married couple has three times as many sons as daughters. If they have two daughters, the size of the family, including parents, is
   (A) 5 (B) 7 (C) 8 (D) 10 (E) 12

1989-G7-6

2. If 6 is one-third of a number, then twice the number is
   (A) 2 (B) 4 (C) 12 (D) 18 (E) 36

1991-G7-10

3. Chris ate $\frac{3}{5}$ of the cookies that Dale baked. If Chris ate 15 cookies, the number of cookies left for Dale was

(A) 9 (B) 25 (C) 12 (D) 6 (E) 10

1988-G7-12

4. When half of a number is increased by 15, the result is 39. The original number is

(A) 108 (B) 54 (C) 48 (D) 27 (E) 12

1978-G-7

5. When 7 is added to half of N, the result is 21. N equals

(A) 7 (B) 28 (C) 14 (D) 56 (E) 49

1976-G-13

6. If $x + 5 = 26 + 4x$, then x equals

(A) 7 (B) –7 (C) $\frac{31}{5}$ (D) $\frac{1}{6}$ (E) $\frac{31}{3}$

1991-G7-4

7. If $\frac{4}{7} \times n = \frac{8}{14}$, then n is

(A) 2 (B) $\frac{4}{7}$ (C) $\frac{1}{2}$ (D) 1 (E) $\frac{2}{7}$

1977-G-19

8. If $x + 2y = 3$, then y is equal to

(A) $\frac{x-3}{2}$ (B) $\frac{3-x}{2}$ (C) $\frac{x+3}{2}$ (D) $\frac{3}{2}$ (E) none of these

1979-G-8

9. A small foreign car uses 12 litres of gas to make a 144 km trip. The number of litres of gas required by this car to travel 336 km would be

(A) 84 (B) 28 (C) 21 (D) 18 (E) 112

1988-G7-4

10. At one time, eggs sold for 12¢ a dozen. At that time, the cost of 151 eggs, in cents, was

(A) 1812 (B) 1510 (C) 1207 (D) 151 (E) 127

1992-G8-10

11. Jeri doubled a number and then added 4 to get 42. If she had first added 4 to the original number and then doubled the result, the answer would have been

(A) 42 (B) 92 (C) 54 (D) 19 (E) 46

1992-G7-7

12. If she works 8 hours a day, Nancy can paint a house is 12 days. If she works only 6 hours a day, the number of days it would take her to paint the same house, working at the same rate, is

(A) 96 (B) 16 (C) 9 (D) 48 (E) 72

1985-G7-25

13. Henry has $24 more than my cousin Joe who has $15 more than my friend Ann. Together the three people have $99. The amount Ann has, in dollars, is

(A) 15 (B) 20 (C) 39 (D) 45 (E) 60

1985-G7-12

14. Sales of baseball gloves at a local store totalled $473. If each glove sold for the same price and if the price is an exact number of dollars, then the number of gloves sold could have been

(A) 7 (B) 9 (C) 11 (D) 13 (E) 15

1984-G-22

15. Wonder Woman gives Superman a five-second head start in a 1 km race. If Wonder Woman runs at 5 km per minute and Superman runs at 3 km per minute, the result of the race is

(A) Wonder Woman wins by 3 seconds
(B) Superman wins by 3 seconds
(C) Superman ties Wonder Woman
(D) Wonder Woman wins by 8 seconds
(E) Superman wins by 13 seconds

Full Solution Questions

1990-G7-3

1. The unit used to weigh diamonds is the carat which is equal to 0.2 g. If the world's largest uncut diamond weighs 969.1 carats, find its weight in grams.

1987-G7-4

2. A certain number is multiplied by 8. The result is then increased by 8. If the final answer is 88, find the original number.

1992-G7-4

3. If twice a number is 36, find three times the number.

1977-G-12

4. Two times a number is increased by 8. If the result is 2 less than three times the number, find the number.

1975-G-6

5. If three pounds of sugar cost $2.85, find the cost of 7 pounds of sugar.

1980-G-7

6. Larry's Diner charges 75 cents for a sandwich, 30 cents for a coffee, and 25 cents for a doughnut. A gentleman paid for two sandwiches, a coffee, and a doughnut, with a five-dollar bill. Determine how much change he received.

1982-P-19

7. If $4a - 3b = 2a + 5b$, find the ratio $b:a$.

1990-G8-4

8. If $(a-1) + a + (a+1) = 27$, find the value of a.

1979-G-4

9. Two numbers are in the ratio 3:5 and their sum is 40. Find the larger number.

1983-G-23

10. A big burger, an order of fries, and a soft drink cost $2.90. Two big burgers, an order of fries, and a soft drink cost $4.40. A big burger with a soft drink costs $2.10. If Eddie orders three big burgers, two orders of fries, and a soft drink, determine how much it will cost him.

1990-G7-24

11. Kit runs around a track in 60 seconds. Sandy, running in the opposite direction, meets Kit every 20 seconds. Find the number of seconds it takes Sandy to run around the track.

1985-P-10

12. A fudge recipe requires $\frac{1}{2}$ cup of milk, $\frac{1}{2}$ cup of maple syrup, $\frac{1}{2}$ cup of butter, and 3 cups of sugar. Find the ratio of maple syrup to the entire mixture.

1980-G-25

13. Some students decide to split equally the cost of a $3.00 pizza. When it arrives, two of the students find they have no money and the remaining students have to pay an extra 40 cents each. Find the number of students originally involved.

1992-G7-23

14. If three positive integers are added two at a time, the sums are 180, 208, and 222. Find the greatest of the three integers.

1992-G8-16

15. Find the difference if the sum of the first 60 positive even integers is subtracted from the sum of the first 61 positive odd integers.

A dart board consists of three circles as shown. The inner circle is worth 5 points, the middle ring is worth 3 points, and the outer ring is worth 2 points. Find the smallest number of darts that can be thrown to earn a score of exactly 21.

Counting and Logic - II

Multiple Choice Questions

1990-G7-4

1. The word MATHEMATICS is to be centered in a space allowing 37 letters. No spaces are permitted between the letters. The number of blank spaces that the typist must leave before starting to type the word is

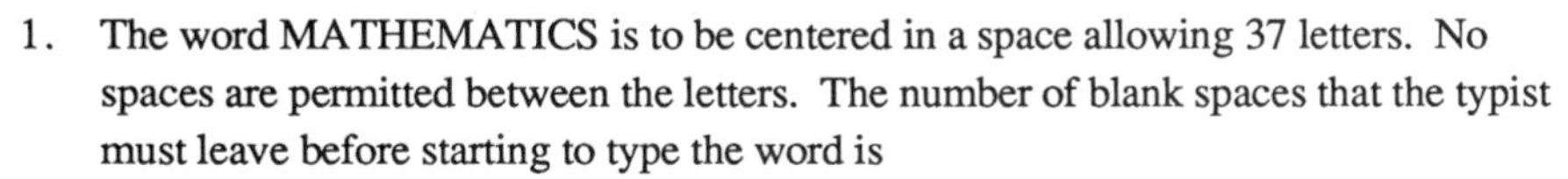

(A) 11 (B) 12 (C) 13 (D) 14 (E) 26

1990-G8-5

2. If K is a point $\frac{2}{3}$ of the way from J to L on the number line shown, the number located at K is

J K L
18 93

(A) 50 (B) 56 (C) 62
(D) 68 (E) 80

1984-G-20

3. If $\frac{p}{q} = -1$, then $p + q$ is

(A) $2p$ (B) $2q$ (C) $-2p$ (D) $-2q$ (E) 0

1991-F-4

4. Lorie is one-third of the way up a flight of stairs. If she climbs 11 more steps, she will be half way up. The number of steps in the flight is

(A) 132 (B) 66 (C) 44 (D) 33 (E) 22

1978-G-18

5. At a party, exactly 15 people ate hot dogs, and exactly 12 people ate hamburgers. Ten of them ate both. Three people ate neither. The number of people at the party was

(A) 20 (B) 40 (C) 35 (D) 30 (E) 18

1992-G8-6

6. When 6 357 829 is multiplied by 48 164, the answer is

(A) 306218476 (B) 394853296
(C) 3497823964896 (D) 306218475956
(E) 317218474952

1975-G-18

7. If $y = -2$, then the number which is greatest is

(A) $2y$ (B) $-\frac{2}{y}$ (C) $\frac{3}{4}y$ (D) $-y^2$ (E) $\frac{1}{8}y^2$

1982-G-20

8. When doing a series of additions on a calculator, a student noted that she added 35 095 instead of 35.95. In order to correct this error with a single entry she should now

(A) add 35.95 (B) subtract 35 059.05 (C) subtract 35 130.95
(D) add 35 130.95 (E) subtract 35 095

1982-G-15

9. Each letter in the subtraction that follows represents a single digit.

$$\begin{array}{r} 6\ p\ q\ r \\ k\ 3\ 5\ 9 \\ \hline 1\ 5\ 8\ 8 \end{array}$$

The letters k, p, q, and r, in order, are

(A) 4, 3, 9, 7 (B) 5, 9, 4, 7 (C) 5, 3, 9, 7 (D) 5, 1, 3, 7 (E) 4, 5, 0, 7

1976-G-16

10. If $\frac{a}{b} = \frac{c}{d}$, and $c \neq d$, which of the following is not true?

(A) $\frac{b}{a} = \frac{d}{c}$ (B) $a^2d^2 = b^2c^2$ (C) $\frac{a}{c} = \frac{b}{d}$

(D) $\frac{a}{d} = \frac{b}{c}$ (E) $\frac{a+b}{b} = \frac{c+d}{d}$

1992-G7-22

11. The number of prime numbers less than ten thousand with digits that have a sum of 2 or 3 is

(A) 4 (B) 3 (C) 6 (D) 5 (E) 2

1992-P-13

12. There are 15 Blue Jays and 14 Orioles perched in 3 trees. Each tree has at least 4 Blue Jays and 2 Orioles. If no tree has more Orioles than Blue Jays, then the largest number of birds that can be in one tree is

(A) 14 (B) 12 (C) 13 (D) 15 (E) 11

Full Solution Questions

1975-G-9

1. A fog horn sounds a blast for 2 seconds and then is silent for 8 seconds. How many blasts are made in a $3\frac{1}{2}$ hour period?

1978-G-13

2. A basketball tournament has 16 teams entered. If each team continues to play in the tournament until beaten once, what is the number of games needed to determine the tournament champion?

1979-G-12

3. At a party, three 8-slice pizzas are ordered for five students. If each student eats the same number of slices, find the number of slices that could be left over.

1985-G7-20

4. A palindromic number reads the same backwards and forwards. For example 1881 is a palindrome. What are the next three years after 1881 that are palindrome numbers?

1991-P-9

5. A dart board consists of three circles as shown. The inner circle is worth 5 points, the middle ring is worth 3 points, and the outer ring is worth 2 points. Find the smallest number of darts that can be thrown to earn a score of exactly 21.

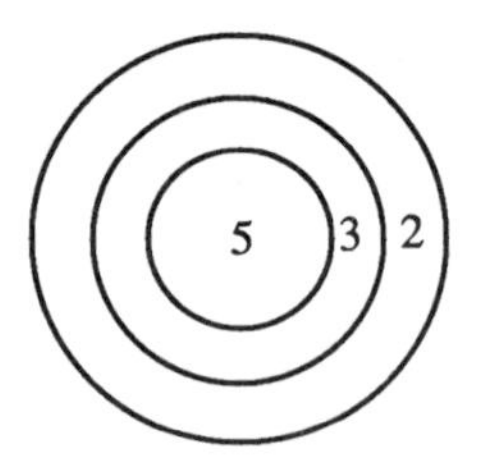

1980-G-24

6. Rearranging the digits of the number 579 produces different three digit numbers. What is the sum of all such numbers, including 579?

1992-G8-9

7. Find the least positive integer by which 24 could be multiplied to give a perfect square.

1991-G7-14

8. In a class of 30 students, twelve played in the band, and seventeen played volleyball. Of these, five students did both. How many students did not participate in either activity?

1988-G7-22

9. Possible values of x are 4, 5, 6, 7, or 8, and possible values of y are 20, 24, 32, 36, or 40. Determine the least and greatest values of $\frac{y}{x}$.

1990-P-8

10. Fred and Joe are playing a game in which the winner receives 25 cents from the loser. Fred has won four games and Joe has $1.25 more than he had at the beginning. Find the least number of games that must have been played.

1982-G-24

11. At a family reunion of 12 people, the official photographer takes pictures of two people at a time. If each person has his picture taken with each of the other people, determine the minimum number of pictures that could be taken.

1987-G7-25

12. If December contains five Sundays in a particular year, then on what days may December 25 occur?

1992-G8-23

13. Your task is to house pigeons in cages so that each cage contains at least one pigeon and no two cages contain the same number of pigeons. Find the maximum number of cages that can be used to house 100 pigeons.

2-Dimensional Geometry - II

Multiple Choice Questions

1983-G-2

1. Angle BCD, in degrees, is

   (A) 74 (B) 98 (C) 76
   (D) 100 (E) 86

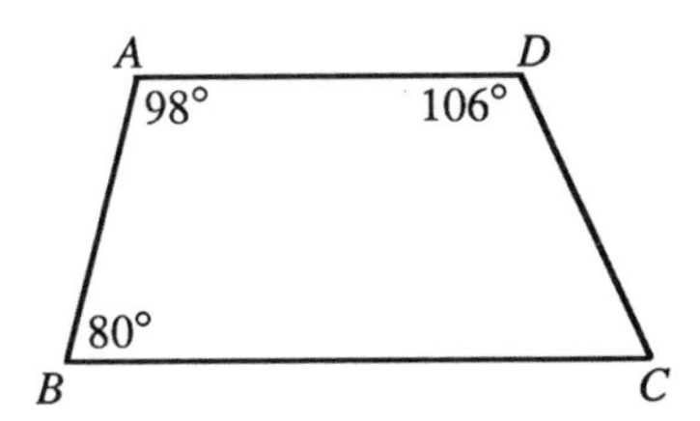

1976-G-11

2. One angle of a triangle is twice the size of the second angle, and the third angle is 66°. The smallest angle, in degrees, is

   (A) 66 (B) 33 (C) 38 (D) 24 (E) 22

1983-G-15

3. Angle *ABD*, in degrees, is

   (A) 110 (B) 57 (C) 80

   (D) 137 (E) 43

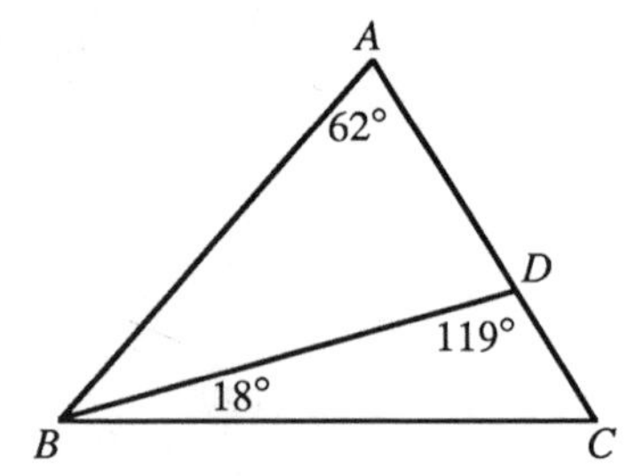

1992-P-6

4. In the diagram, the value of *y* is

   (A) 60 (B) 20 (C) 30

   (D) 50 (E) 40

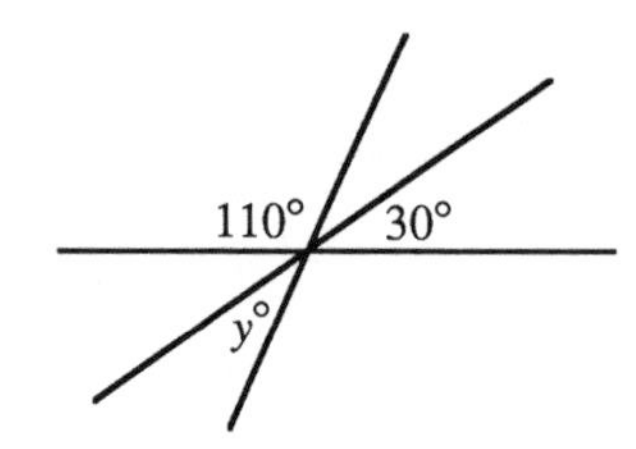

1983-G-8

5. Three given line segments have lengths of 4 cm, 5 cm, and 6 cm. The three line segments will

   (A) not form a triangle (B) form an isosceles triangle

   (C) form a scalene triangle (D) form an equilateral triangle

   (E) form a right-angled triangle

1985-G8-4

6. The triangle at the right is reflected using the x-axis as a mirror-line. The triangle below which represents the mirror image is

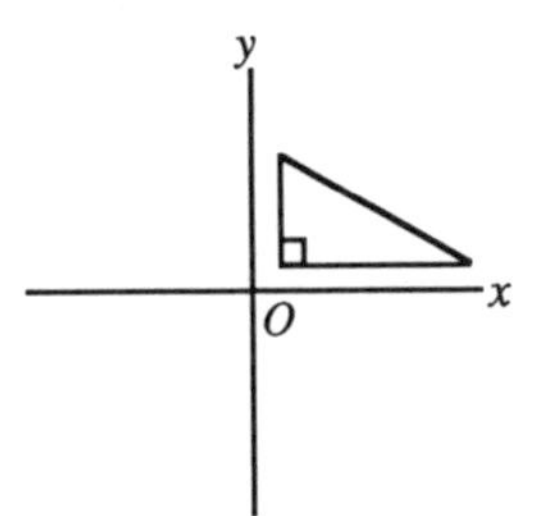

(A)

(B)

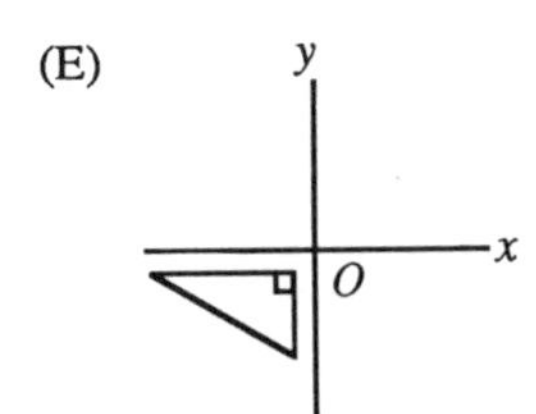

(C)

(D)

(E)

1991-G8-5

7. The number of lines of symmetry of the given figure is

(A) 3 (B) 1 (C) 6
(D) 12 (E) 2

1991-G8-17

8. The graph shows how Pat distributes her weekly earnings of \$120. To make the size of each sector proportional to the amount distributed, the angle x, in degrees, is

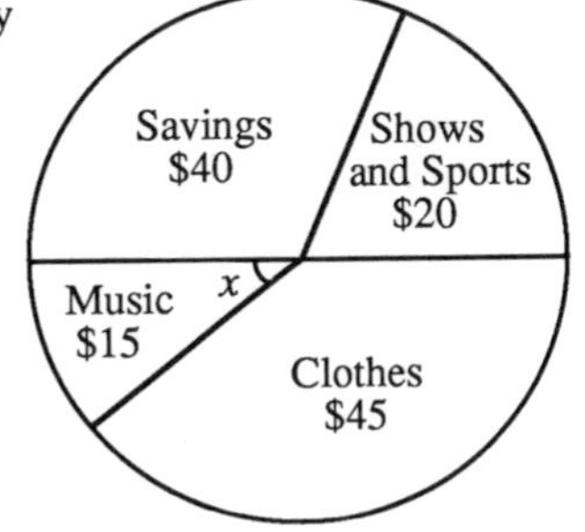

(A) 12.5 (B) 22.5 (C) 36
(D) 45 (E) 51.4

1990-P-10

9. Two sides of a triangle have lengths 14 and 18. Of the following lengths, the one that ***cannot*** be that of the third side is

(A) 2 (B) 6 (C) 7 (D) 28 (E) 30

1992-G8-11

10. Three diameters, AB, PQ, and ST divide the circle into six equal sectors. Each diameter is 18 cm long. Of the answers given, the closest approximation of the area of the shaded sectors, in cm^2, is

(A) 200 (B) 800 (C) 100
(D) 700 (E) 300

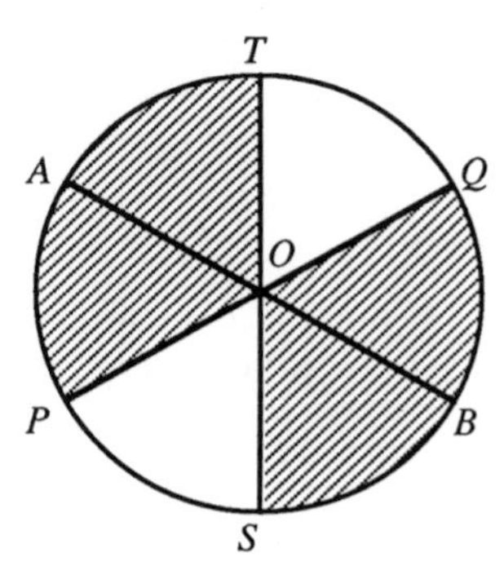

1986-G8-13

11. A sailboat leaves the dock and sails 12 km west, then 9 km north. At this time, its shortest distance from the dock, in km, is

(A) 3 (B) 15 (C) 21 (D) 108 (E) 225

1984-G-10

12. A 1.8 m stick casts an 80 cm shadow. At the same time, a tower casts a 400 cm shadow. The height of the tower, in metres, is

(A) 0.36 (B) 3.6 (C) 9 (D) 90 (E) 900

1975-G-19

13. A ladder 26 metres long is placed against a wall so that the top of the ladder is 24 metres above the base of the wall. The distance, in metres, from the base of the wall to the foot of the ladder is

(A) 2 (B) 4 (C) 100 (D) 10 (E) $\sqrt{1252}$

1988-G7-7

14. The triangle shown is reflected in the line which passes through the dots labelled 4, 5, and 6. The vertices of the reflected triangle will be located at dots labelled

(A) 3, 4, 8 (B) 1, 4, 8 (C) 2, 4, 9
(D) 2, 6, 7 (E) 1, 6, 8

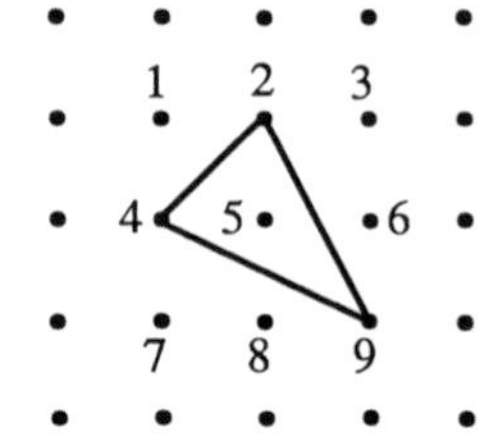

1992-G8-25

15. The perimeter of the rectangle shown is 40 cm and one of its dimentions is x cm. Different rectangles with the same perimeter are drawn. The graph that shows the relationship between the area of the rectangle and the value of x is

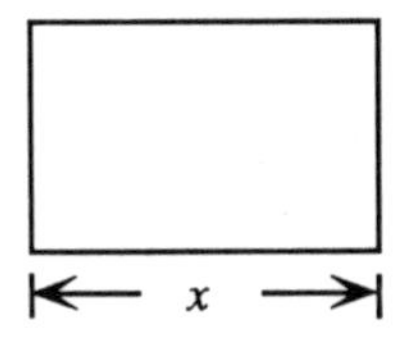

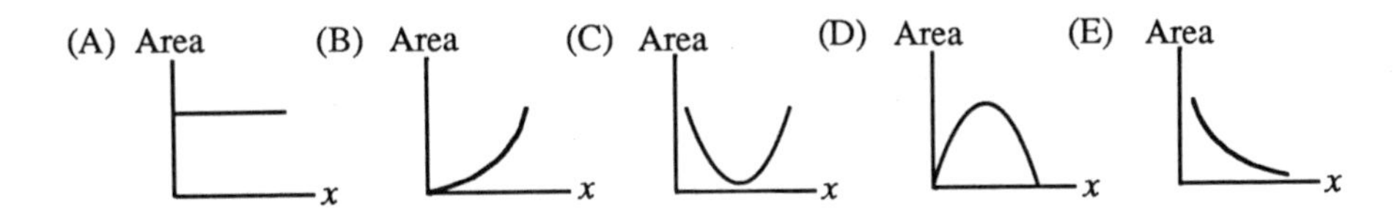

Full Solution Questions

1985-G7-18

1. In ΔABC, $\angle A = 120°$ and angle B is five times angle C. Find the number of degrees in angle C.

1990-C-3

2. The angles of a triangle are in the ratio 2:5:11. Find the smallest angle.

1992-G8-8

3. In the diagram, the measure of angle PRQ is 120° and the measure of angle PST is 110°. Find the measure of angle RPS.

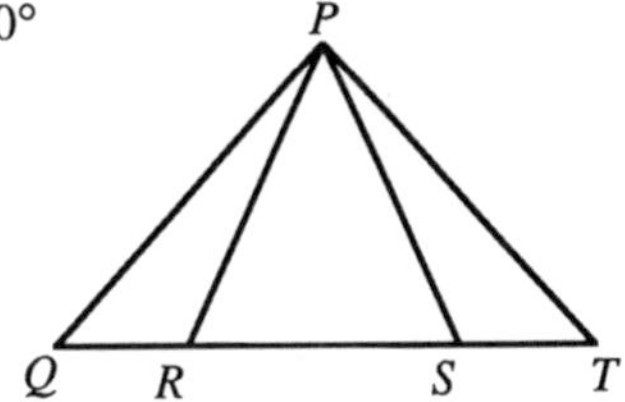

1977-G-11

4. In the diagram $\angle A = 40°$. Find the size of $\angle DBC$.

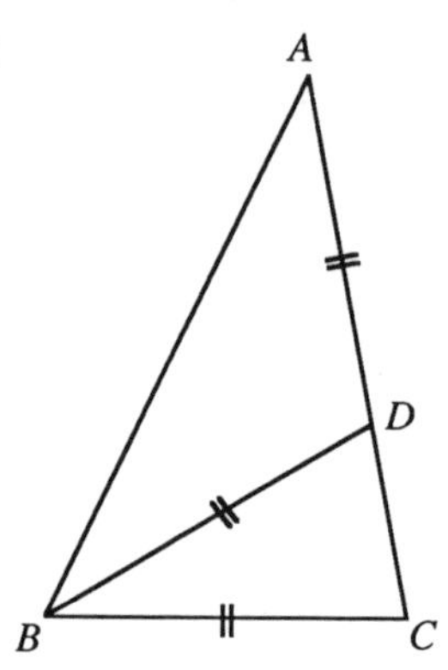

1981-G-23

5. In the diagram, $AB = 15$ cm, $DB = 6$ cm, $BC = 8$ cm, and $\angle B = 90°$. Find the perimeter of ΔADC.

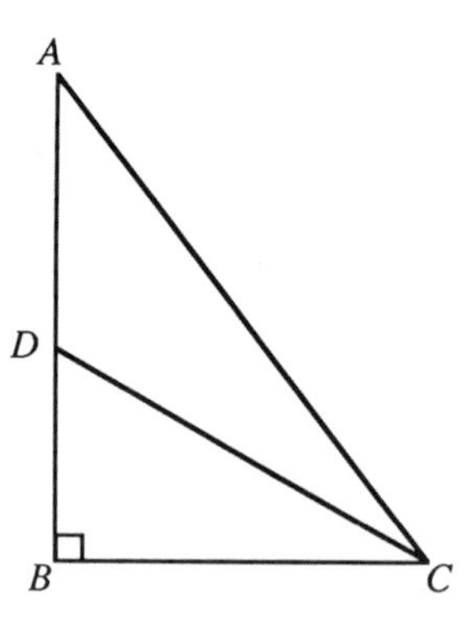

1986-G7-7

6. The midpoints of the sides of a rectangle are joined as shown. Find the fraction of the rectangle which is shaded.

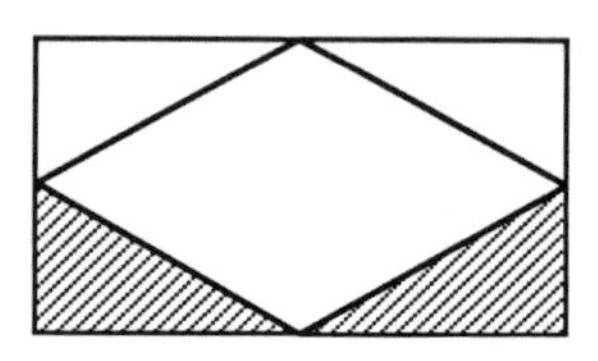

1985-G8-24

7. Jakob has a box of T-shaped tiles like the one in the diagram. Each of the seven short segments has the same length. He wishes to form a rectangle, which is not a square, using these tiles without overlapping any of the tiles. Find the minimum number of tiles required to form the rectangle.

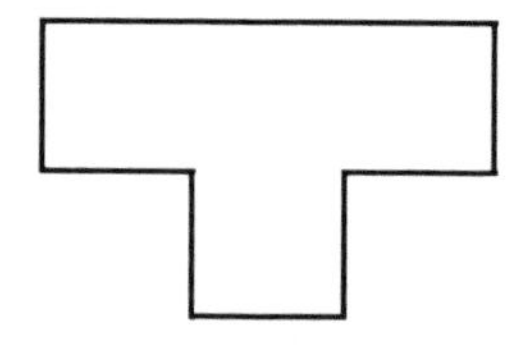

1992-F-3

8. In the diagram, find the length of AD.

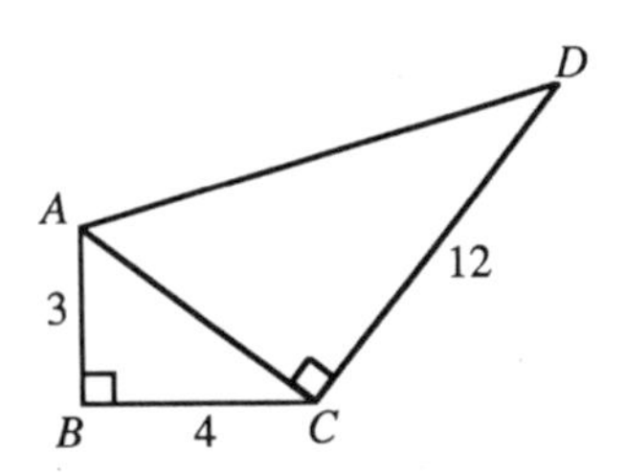

1991-G8-12

9. A, B, and C are three points indicated on a number line. Find the fraction that AB is of AC.

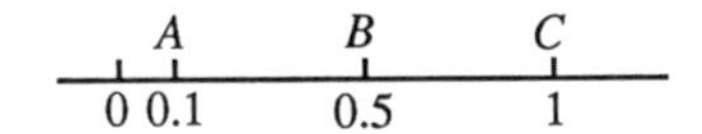

1982-G-18

10. Find the size of the angle which the minute hand of a clock sweeps out between 8:15 a.m. and 8:40 a.m.

1991-P-8

11. $ABCD$ is a rectangle. $AB = BE$ and $\angle AEF = 86°$. Determine the measure of $\angle AFE$.

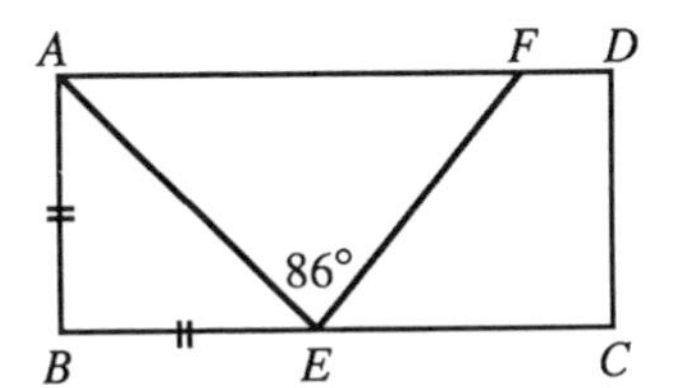

1991-G8-16

12. In the quadrilateral $PQRS$, angle P is 120° and angle Q is four times angle S. If angle R is 90°, find the number of degrees in angle S.

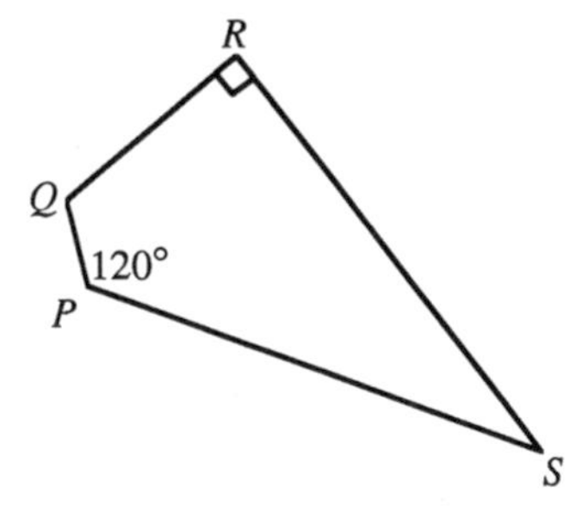

1986-G7-18

13. A camera takes a picture of a metre-stick beside a brick wall. In the developed picture the metre-stick is 2 cm long and the brick wall is 4.5 cm high. Find the actual height of the brick wall.

1990-G7-23

14. A 70 cm by 84 cm rectangle is entirely covered by identical square tiles. Find the least number of tiles required.

If a school has 420 students and 20 of them are on the basketball team, what is the ratio of basketball players to non-basketball players?

Number Patterns and Sequences - II

Multiple Choice Questions

1984-G-8

1. The sum $1 + 3 + 5 + 7 + 9 + 11$ is the square of

   (A) 6 (B) 18 (C) 36 (D) 286 (E) 1296

1982-G-11

2. Starting at 7 and counting by 13s, a student counts 7, 20, 33, etc. A number that will be counted is

   (A) 70 (B) 71 (C) 72 (D) 73 (E) 74

1977-G-21

3. $2^2 - 1^2 = 3$, $4^2 - 3^2 = 7$, $6^2 - 5^2 = 11$, etc. The sum of $10^2 - 9^2 + 8^2 - 7^2 + 6^2 - 5^2 + 4^2 - 3^2 + 2^2 - 1^2$ is

(A) 5 (B) –55 (C) –5 (D) 25 (E) 55

1985-G7-5

4. The value of
$1 + 2 + 3 + 4 + 5 + 6 + 7 + 8 + 9 + 10 + 9 + 8 + 7 + 6 + 5 + 4 + 3 + 2 + 1$ is

(A) 90 (B) 94 (C) 100 (D) 106 (E) 110

1983-G-17

5. In the expression $n^2 - 4n$, the n is replaced by 1, then by 2, and then by 3. The product of the resulting three numbers is

(A) 36 (B) –36 (C) –10 (D) 12 (E) –12

1978-G-3

6. If a school has 420 students and 20 of them are on the basketball team, the ratio of basketball players to non-basketball players is

(A) 420:20 (B) 20:420 (C) 400:20 (D) 20:400 (E) 105:4

1986-G8-10

7. Notice that $\frac{1}{9} = 0.1111...$, $\frac{32}{99} = 0.3232...$, and $\frac{785}{999} = 0.785785...$. Using this pattern, 0.41144114... equals

(A) $\frac{41}{99}$ (B) $\frac{411}{999}$ (C) $\frac{4114}{9999}$ (D) $\frac{41\,144}{99\,999}$ (E) $\frac{411\,441}{999\,999}$

1992-G7-3

8. If the points shown on the number line are equally spaced, the number at Q is

M N O P Q R S
0 15

(A) 14 (B) 10 (C) 12
(D) 9 (E) 11

1990-C-9

9. If the square root of a number is between 6 and 7, then the cube root of this number is between

(A) 1 and 2 (B) 2 and 3 (C) 3 and 4 (D) 4 and 5 (E) 5 and 6

1992-G8-15

10. A mite is a microscopic insect 0.00002 cm in length. The number of mites doubles in number every 30 minutes. One hour ago there were 50 000 in a room. If the mites now present were placed end to end in a line, then the length of this line, in centimetres, would be
(A) 0.5 (B) 1 (C) 2 (D) 3 (E) 4

1974-G-23

11. A sequence is 1, 2, 5, 10, 17, ... A possible seventh number in this sequence is
(A) 24 (B) 26 (C) 37 (D) 50 (E) none of these

1992-G7-24

12. At midnight on January 1, Pat snapped his fingers. One second later, he snapped his fingers again. After an interval of two seconds he snapped his fingers again. He snapped his fingers again after an interval of four seconds and again after an interval of eight seconds, and so on. Pat continued this pattern with the time interval between snaps doubling at each stage. Of the following, the best approximation to the number of times he would snap his fingers in a year would be
(A) 30 (B) 25 (C) 1024 (D) 15 (E) 20

Full Solution Questions

1986-G8-11

1. When Karl Friedrich Gauss was a young lad he discovered that the sum, S, of the first n natural numbers is given by the formula
$$S = \frac{n(n+1)}{2}.$$
Find the sum of the first 30 natural numbers.

1986-G8-9

2. My rich uncle gave me one dollar for my first birthday. On each birthday after that, he doubled his previous gift. What was the total amount he had given me up to and including my eighth birthday?

1988-G7-9

3. One plant is now 12 cm tall and will grow 2 cm per week. A second plant is now 3 cm tall and will grow 5 cm per week. How many weeks does it take before the plants are the same height?

1974-G-21

4. Find the sum of all the odd integers from 1 to 99 inclusive.

1991-G7-11

5. The sum of the digits in the year 1991 is 20; that is, $1 + 9 + 9 + 1 = 20$. Determine the number of years between 1900 and 1999 whose digits have a sum of 20.

1982-G-14

6. The ratio of girls to boys to teachers in a school is 7:5:1. If there are 50 teachers, find the total number of girls, boys, and teachers in the school.

1991-G8-11

7. Canadian coins are made in six denominations: 1¢, 5¢, 10¢, 25¢, 50¢, and $1.00. Find the number of different ways 18¢ can be made from these coins.

1986-G7-17

8. Find the sum of the digits in the tens place of all two digit whole numbers.

1991-G8-19

9. A palindromic number is the same whether read from right to left or from left to right. For example, 121 and 4334 are palindromic numbers. The number of palindromic numbers between 100 and 200 is a and between 1000 and 2000 is b. Find the value of $b - a$.

1990-G8-23

10. A cyclist rode 410 kilometres in five days. Each day he travelled 15 km more than he rode the previous day. Find the distance travelled on the first day.

1992-G8-12

11. Mr. Digme planted five primroses along one side of his property. He then planted one poppy plant in each of the spaces between the primroses. Next he planted peonies in each of the spaces between the plants already in the line. He then repeated this procedure with petunias and then with pansies. Determine the total number of plants in the row.

1989-G8-21

12. Find the sum of all the digits of all the numbers in the sequence 1, 2, 3, ..., 99, 100.

1990-F-13

13. Find the sum of the first 25 terms of the sequence $1, 2, -3, 4, 5, -6, 7, 8, -9, \ldots$.

3-Dimensional Geometry - II

Multiple Choice Questions

1990-G7-5

1. A square sheet of metal has four smaller squares removed from the corners, as shown in the diagram. The metal is folded along the dotted lines to form an open box having base 6 cm by 6 cm and volume 72 cm^3. The height of the box, in cm, is

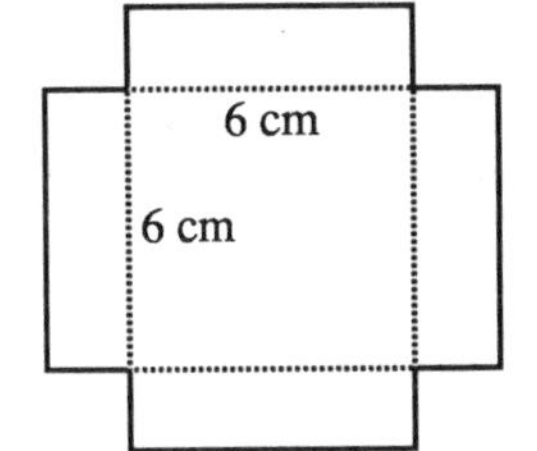

(A) 1 (B) 2 (C) 3
(D) 4 (E) 6

1989-G7-12

2. The longest side of a rectangular box is 10 m. The shortest side is 6 m. Of the following, the number which could represent the volume of the box, in m^3, is
(A) 60 (B) 120 (C) 300 (D) 480 (E) 720

1991-G7-13

3. When the figure is cut out and folded to make a cube, the letter W is on one face. The letter on the opposite face is
(A) X (B) S (C) R
(D) V (E) K

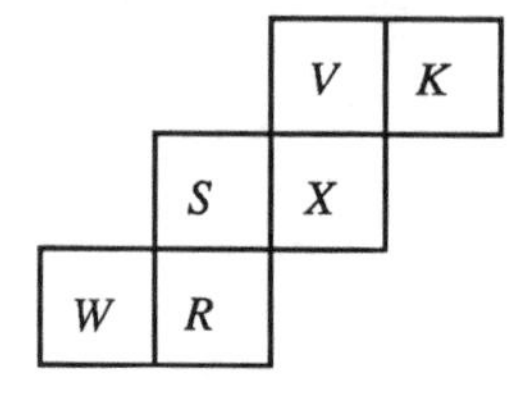

1988-G7-16

4. Three cuts are made through a large cube to make eight identical smaller cubes. The total surface area of the smaller cubes is
(A) one-eighth of the surface area of the larger cube
(B) one-half of the surface area of the larger cube
(C) double the surface area of the larger cube
(D) eight times the surface area of the larger cube
(E) the same as the surface area of the larger cube

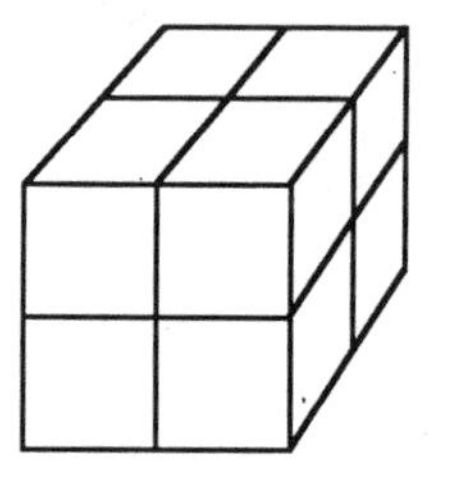

1992-G8-17

5. The areas of three of the faces of the rectangular box shown are 10 cm^2, 12 cm^2, and 30 cm^2. The volume of the box, in cm^3, is
(A) 60 (B) 52 (C) 3600
(D) 300 (E) 120

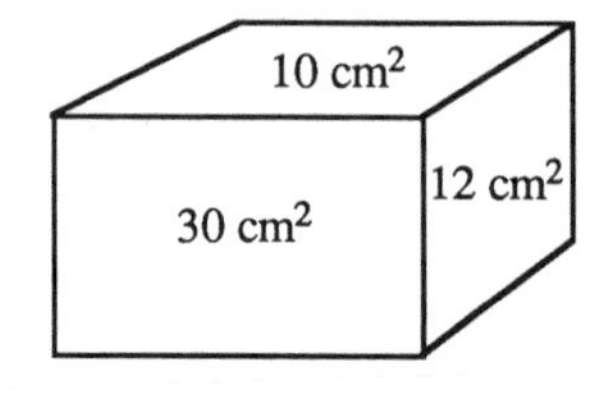

1986-G7-20

6. The figure below which can be obtained by rotating the figure on the right is

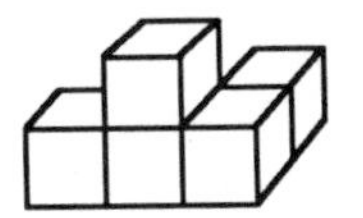

(A)

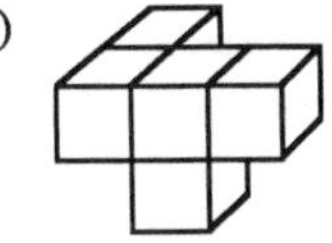

(B)

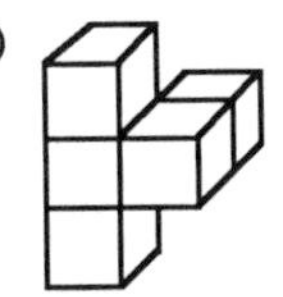

(C)

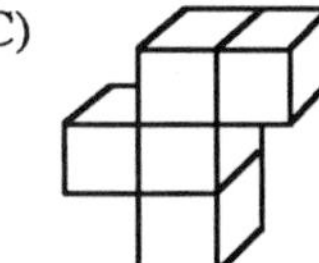

(D)

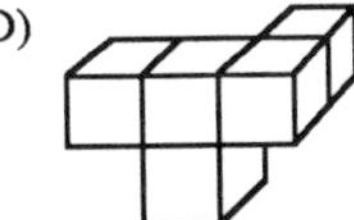

(E)

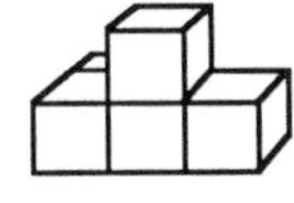

1992-G7-21

7. In the illustrated solid, the steps are of equal width and equal height. The volume of this solid, in cm^3, is

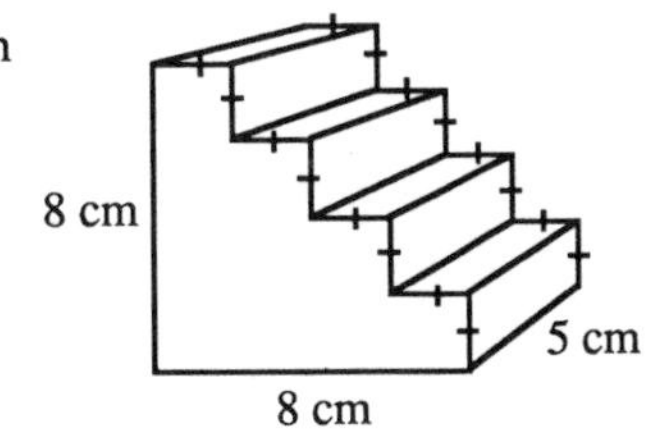

(A) 200 (B) 320 (C) 21
(D) 80 (E) 160

1991-G8-20

8. A fly is walking along the edges of a 10 cm cube. The fly never walks along any edge more than once. The greatest distance, in centimetres, that the fly can walk is

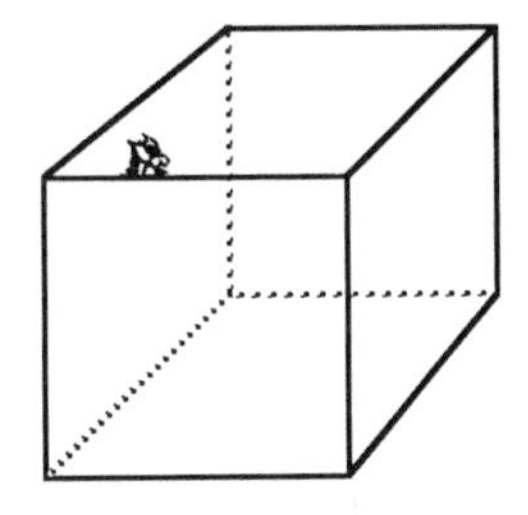

(A) 40 (B) 60 (C) 30
(D) 90 (E) 120

1992-P-19

9. A $3 \times 3 \times 3$ cube, a $2 \times 2 \times 2$ cube, and a $1 \times 1 \times 1$ cube are glued together as shown. The total surface area of this object, including the bottom, is

(A) 36 (B) 74 (C) 84
(D) 65 (E) 79

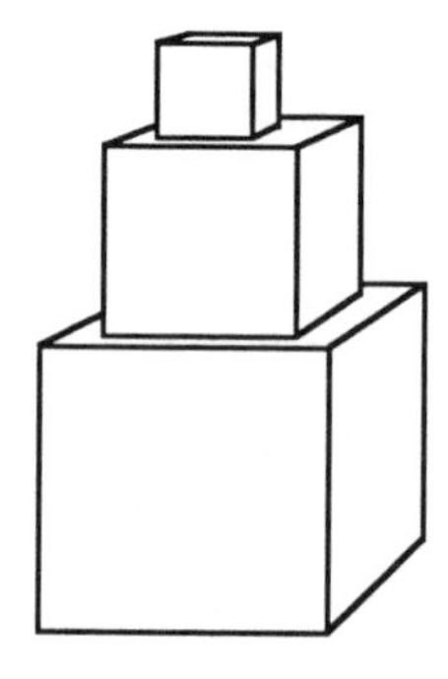

1989-G8-22

10. A 3 cm by 3 cm by 4 cm block is built from 1 cm cubes, each of which is coloured red or white. If the colours of the individual cubes alternate, the number of red faces which are hidden from sight in the interior of the block is

(A) 42 (B) 54 (C) 69 (D) 75 (E) 108

1990-C-10

11. A cylindrical container having an inside diameter of 60 cm and height h is filled with water. The number of cylinders, with inside diameter of 10 cm and height h, required to hold the same volume of water is

(A) 6 (B) 12 (C) 18 (D) 36 (E) 216

1991-P-24

12. An ice cube tray has two section as shown. Each section is 4 cm high, 4 cm long, and 3 cm wide. One section is full of water; the other is half full.

If the tray is tipped at a 45° angle towards the half full section, the volume of water that spills out, in cm^3, is

(A) 0 (B) 8 (C) 12
(D) 24 (E) 3

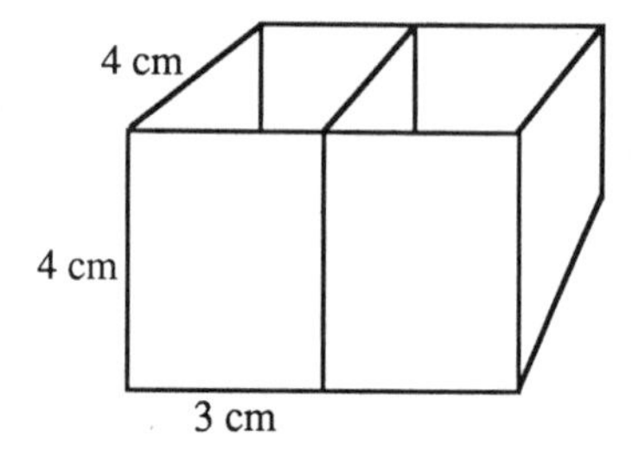

Full Solution Questions

1981-G-22

1. A base row of blocks is formed and rows of blocks are added so that each new row has one fewer blocks than the row below it. If the base has nine blocks and the final row has one block, what is the total number of blocks used?

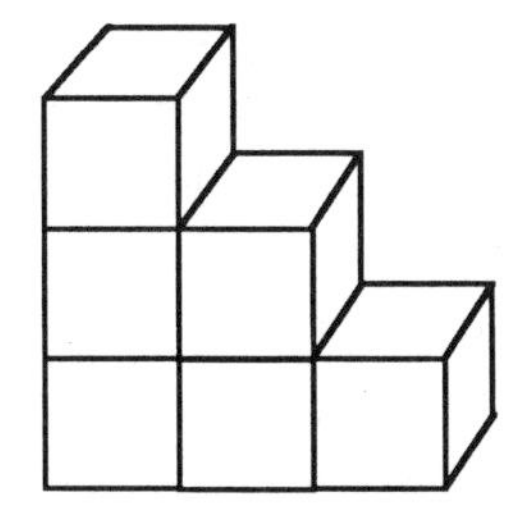

1992-G7-11

2. A cubic block of cheese is to be cut into eight identical pieces. Determine the least number of knife cuts required.

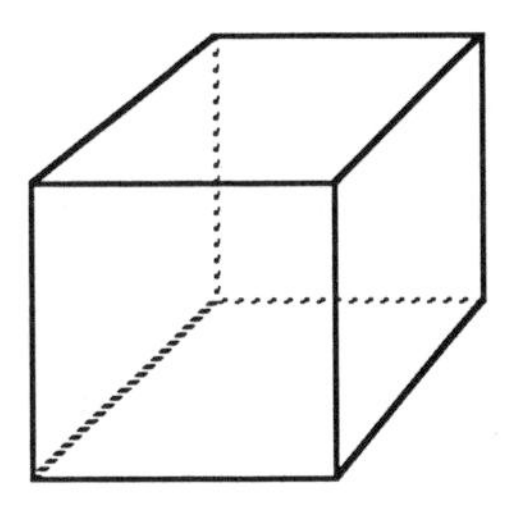

1986-G8-19

3. A cube has a surface area of 24 cm^2. What is the volume of the cube?

1991-G8-13

4. Find the volume, in cm^3, of the T-shaped solid shown.

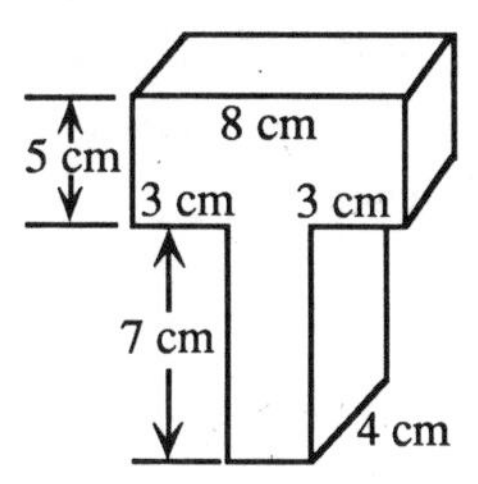

1991-G8-24

5. The numbers on the faces of a regular die are arranged so that opposite faces total 7; for example, 2 is opposite 5. The four dice shown have been placed so that the two numbers on the faces touching each other always total 9.
The face labelled *P* is the front of one die as shown. What is the number on the face labelled *P*?

1992-G8-21

6. Five cubes are arranged as shown in the diagram. The edge length of each cube is twice the edge length of the cube to its right. The middle cube has volume $64\ cm^3$. Determine the total volume of the five cubes.

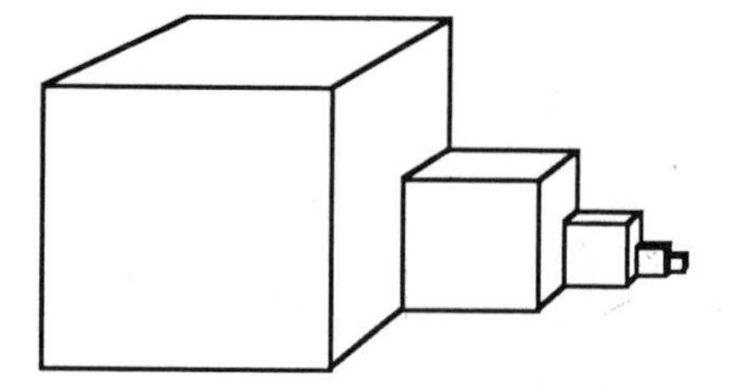

1984-P-13

7. A rectangular box has dimensions 9 cm by 6 cm by 24 cm. A second rectangular box has volume one-half of the first and has a base 6 cm by 4 cm. What is the height of the second box?

1983-G-22

8. The diagram shows a soup can with the top and bottom removed. The diameter of the can is 5 cm and the height is 12 cm. If the can is cut along the dotted line, what is the perimeter of the resulting rectangle?

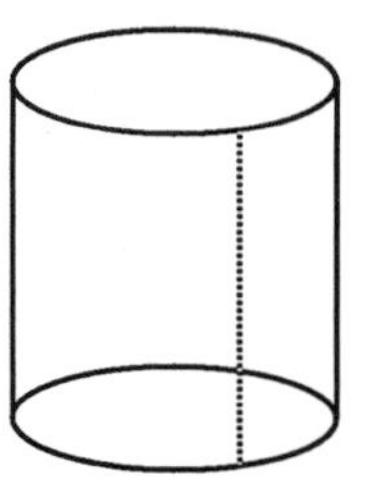

1983-G-25

9. The diagram shows a painted rectangular solid. The solid was then cut along the dotted lines into 12 identical rectangular blocks. What is the total area of all the unpainted surfaces?

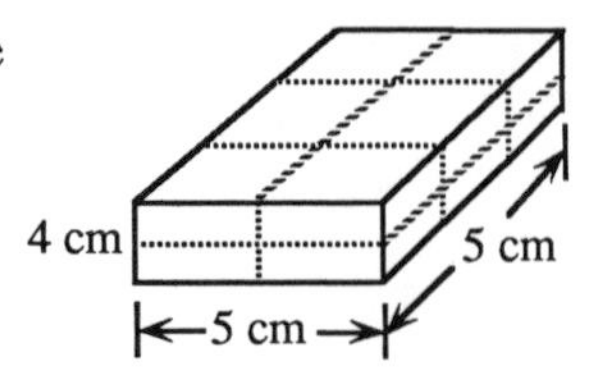

1965-J-24

10. A rectangular container with base 9 cm by 11 cm has a height of 38.5 cm. Assuming that water expands 10% when it freezes, determine the depth to which the container can be filled so that when the contents freeze, the ice does not go above the top edge of the container.

1989-G8-25

11. A plane cuts a block through the midpoints of the three edges as marked. The smaller piece is discarded. What is the volume of the remaining part of the block?

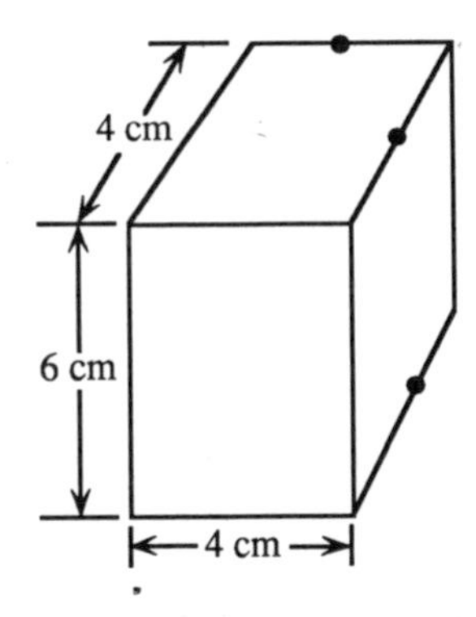

1990-G8-25

12. A 5 by 5 by 5 cube is formed using 1 by 1 by 1 cubes. A number of smaller cubes are removed by punching out the 15 designated columns from front to back, top to bottom, and side to side. How many smaller cubes remain?

The town of Canton is west of Mason. Sinclair is east of Canton but west of Mason. Dexter is east of Richmond but west of both Sinclair and Canton. Of the five towns, which one is farthest west?

Miscellaneous and Challenge Problems

Multiple Choice Questions

1991-G7-21

1. Bill and Mary are planting trees for the town. On the first day, they planted 38 trees. Bill didn't work on the second day but Mary planted the same number she had the first day. They had now planted 60 trees. The number of trees that Bill planted was

(A) 19 (B) 22 (C) 38 (D) 20 (E) 16

1981-G-3

2. $\sqrt{36} - \sqrt{16}$ equals

(A) 2 (B) $\sqrt{2}$ (C) $\sqrt{6} - \sqrt{4}$ (D) 10 (E) $\sqrt{20}$

1980-G-22

3. The town of Canton is west of Mason. Sinclair is east of Canton but west of Mason. Dexter is east of Richmond but west of both Sinclair and Canton. Of the five towns, the one farthest west is

(A) Mason (B) Dexter (C) Canton (D) Sinclair (E) Richmond

1992-G7-6

4. An historic train, *The King Edward*, leaves Dunnville at 10:56 on its final run to Attridgetown, $2\frac{1}{2}$ hours away. The time at which *The King Edward* arrives in Attridgetown is

(A) 8:26 (B) 9:26 (C) 12:26 (D) 12:56 (E) 1:26

1991-G7-7

5. Toothpaste is packaged in 25 ml, 50 ml, 100 ml, 150 ml, and 250 ml sizes. The largest size is x times the smallest. The value of x is

(A) 2 (B) 225 (C) 10 (D) 100 (E) 0.1

1981-G-2

6. If $\frac{N}{72} = \frac{5}{18}$, N equals

(A) 20 (B) 16 (C) 15 (D) 14 (E) 12

1992-G8-14

7. A car is travelling at 90 km/h. The distance, in metres, it travels in 10 seconds is

(A) 25 (B) 1500 (C) 250 (D) 15 000 (E) 3240

1987-G7-10

8. If Janet travels 48 km in 45 minutes, her speed, in kilometres per hour, is

(A) 60 (B) 36 (C) 64 (D) 70 (E) 63

1991-G7-20

9. The chart shows the distribution of \$1, \$2, \$3, \$4, and \$5 door prizes. The average value of all the door prizes is

(A) \$3 (B) \$0.50 (C) \$4
(D) \$8 (E) \$2

Value of Prize	Number of Prizes
\$ 1	25
\$ 2	20
\$ 3	8
\$ 4	4
\$ 5	3

1992-G8-19

10. The value of $1 - \cfrac{1}{1 - \cfrac{1}{1 - \frac{1}{11}}}$ is

(A) 11 (B) 0 (C) –3 (D) –9 (E) –10

1986-G7-5

11. The greatest possible product of two positive integers which have a sum of 7 is

(A) 12 (B) 6 (C) 7 (D) 14 (E) 10

1988-G8-15

12. Five is a prime number which can be written as the sum of two prime numbers. A number which is a prime number and which ***cannot*** be written as the sum of two prime numbers is

(A) 7 (B) 8 (C) 9 (D) 11 (E) 13

1989-G8-24

13. If m and n are positive integers such that $m^2 - n^2 = 29$, then the product mn

(A) is less than 100
(B) is between 100 and 150
(C) is between 150 and 200
(D) is between 201 and 250 inclusive
(E) is greater than 250

1980-G-19

14. A student uses a calculator to divide two integers and obtains an answer 4.4285714. Without using a calculator yourself, determine which of the following pairs the student could have been using.

(A) 63 and 14
(B) 31 and 7
(C) 44 285 714 and 10
(D) 40 and 9
(E) 199 and 45

Full Solution Questions

1987-G8-23

1. Two towns are 80 km apart. Sylvia wants to drive from one town to the other in exactly one hour. For the first 30 minutes she drives at a rate of 60 km/h. At what constant rate must she drive for the next 30 minutes if she is to accomplish her goal?

1982-G-5

2. The formula which relates Fahrenheit temperature, F, to Celsius temperature, C, is $F = \frac{9}{5}C + 32$. What is the Fahrenheit temperature when the Celsius temperature is -40?

1991-G7-16

3. The average of five different numbers is 4. When the greatest number is removed from the set, the average of the remaining numbers is 2. What number is removed?

1991-G7-23

4. Before beginning an exam, Gerry calculated that, if she were to spend 10 minutes solving each of the 12 problems, then she would be able to complete the exam in 2 hours. During the exam, Gerry found some problems difficult. They each took her twice as long as she had calculated. She found the remaining problems easy. They took only half as long as she calculated. She completed the 12 problems in exactly 2 hours. How many problems did Gerry find to be difficult?

1992-G8-20

5. The five members of a club decided to buy a used microcomputer, splitting the cost equally. Later, three new members joined the club and agreed to pay their share of the purchase price. This resulted in a saving of $15.00 for each of the original five members. What was the original price of the used microcomputer?

1991-G7-18

6. Your secret club shares its earnings. The president receives half of the money. The vice-president gets a quarter of the remainder. Then, the secretary gets a third of what is left. Finally, the treasurer and you share what is left equally. Your share is three dollars. Calculate the club's total earnings.

1991-G7-19

7. A square piece of paper is folded in half vertically, then folded in half horizontally as shown. The resulting figure has a perimeter of 12 cm. Find the area of the original piece of paper.

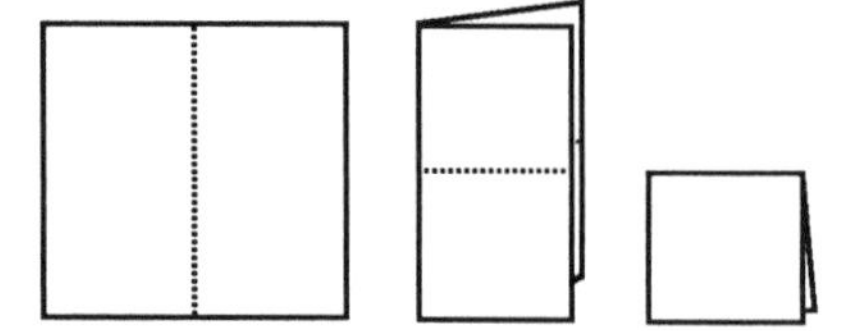

1992-G8-18

8. In a computer game, Super Maria travels through a maze as shown from Start to Finish. She is allowed to travel only east, south, or southeast along a path. Calculate the number of different paths she could take from Start to Finish.

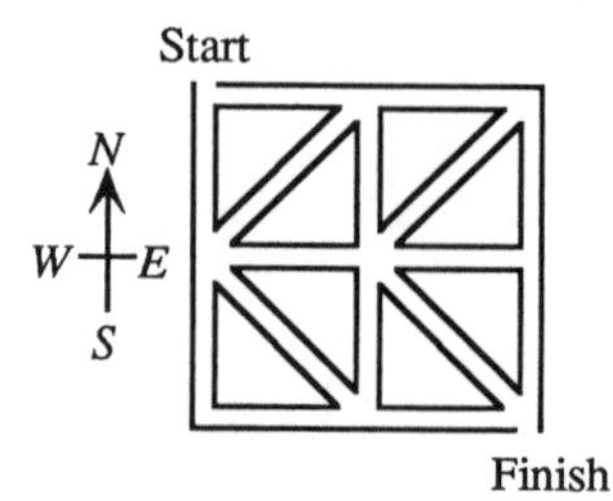

1977-G-15

9. Two numbers have a sum of 8 and a product of 15. Find the sum of the reciprocals of the numbers.

1984-G-21

10. A number greater than 1 is said to be a prime number if its only factors are 1 and itself. Determine the smallest perfect square that has three different prime numbers as factors.

1992-G7-25

11. If x and y are positive integers and $13x + 8y = 1992$, determine the minimum value of $x + y$.

1991-G7-25

12. On Old MacDonald's farm, every two horses share a trough, every three cows share a trough, and every eight pigs share a trough. Old MacDonald has the same number of each animal, and he has a total of 69 troughs. How many animals does Old MacDonald have on his farm?

1988-G7-25

13. Find the number of integers between 100 and 1000 such that the sum of their digits is 10.

1991-G8-25

14. "Baker's Dozen" doughnuts are sold only in boxes of 7, 13, or 25. To buy 14 doughnuts you must order two boxes of 7, but you cannot buy exactly 15 since no combination of boxes contains 15 doughnuts. What is the largest number of doughnuts that cannot be ordered using combinations of these boxes?

Solutions

Fractions

Multiple Choice Questions

1. Solution 1

$$4+\frac{2}{10}+\frac{4}{1000}=4+0.2+0.004$$
$$=4.204$$

Solution 2

$$4+\frac{2}{10}+\frac{4}{1000}=4+\frac{200}{1000}+\frac{4}{1000}$$
$$=4+\frac{204}{1000}$$
$$=4.204$$

The answer is C.

2. Solution

The number is $\frac{5}{8}-\frac{1}{2}=\frac{5}{8}-\frac{4}{8}$
$$=\frac{1}{8}$$

The answer is A.

3. Solution

$$\frac{1}{2}+\frac{1}{3}+\frac{1}{4}+\frac{2}{3}+\frac{2}{4}+\frac{3}{4}=\left(\frac{1}{2}+\frac{2}{4}\right)+\left(\frac{1}{3}+\frac{2}{3}\right)+\left(\frac{1}{4}+\frac{3}{4}\right)$$
$$=1+1+1$$
$$=3$$

The answer is A.

4. Solution

$$1\tfrac{1}{3}\times 1\tfrac{1}{2}=\frac{4}{3}\times\frac{3}{2}$$
$$=\frac{12}{6}$$
$$=2$$

The answer is C.

5. Solution

When $a=2$ and $b=3$, $\frac{1}{a}+\frac{1}{b}=\frac{1}{2}+\frac{1}{3}$
$$=\frac{3}{6}+\frac{2}{6}$$
$$=\frac{5}{6}$$

The answer is E.

6. Solution 1

$$\frac{3}{4}+\frac{5}{2}\times\frac{3}{4}=\frac{3}{4}+\left(\frac{5}{2}\times\frac{3}{4}\right)$$
$$=\frac{3}{4}+\frac{15}{8}$$
$$=\frac{6}{8}+\frac{15}{8}$$
$$=\frac{21}{8}$$

Solution 2

$$\frac{3}{4}+\frac{5}{2}\times\frac{3}{4}=\frac{3}{4}\left(1+\frac{5}{2}\right)$$
$$=\frac{3}{4}\times\frac{7}{2}$$
$$=\frac{21}{8}$$

The answer is B.

7. Solution 1

After thirty-five minutes have elapsed, the time remaining is $60-35=25$ minutes.
The fraction of an hour that this represents is $\frac{25}{60}=\frac{5}{12}$.

Solution 2

On a clock, an hour is divided into 12 intervals of five minutes each.
After thirty-five minutes have elapsed, the time remaining is $60-35=25$ minutes.
These 25 remaining minutes represent $\frac{25}{5}=5$ of the 12 intervals.
Therefore, the time remaining to complete the contest is $\frac{5}{12}$ of an hour.
The answer is E.

8. Solution

$$\frac{7}{3}+\frac{1}{4}=\frac{28}{12}+\frac{3}{12}=\frac{31}{12}$$
$$\frac{7}{9}+\frac{7}{3}=\frac{7}{9}+\frac{21}{9}=\frac{28}{9}$$
$$\frac{4}{7}+\frac{3}{5}=\frac{20}{35}+\frac{21}{35}=\frac{41}{35}$$
$$\frac{1}{4}+\frac{1}{3}=\frac{3}{12}+\frac{4}{12}=\frac{7}{12}$$
$$\frac{1}{2}+\frac{1}{6}=\frac{3}{6}+\frac{1}{6}=\frac{4}{6}$$

The answer is D.

9. Solution

At this rate, it requires 3 hours to fill each $\frac{1}{5}$ of the swimming pool.
To fill the remaining $\frac{2}{5}$ of the pool requires 6 hours.
The answer is D.

10. Solution

$$\left(3\tfrac{1}{3}\right)^2 = \left(\tfrac{10}{3}\right)^2$$
$$= \tfrac{10}{3} \times \tfrac{10}{3}$$
$$= \tfrac{100}{9}$$
$$= 11\tfrac{1}{9}$$

The answer is A.

11. Solution

$$\tfrac{1}{3} + \tfrac{2}{5} \div \tfrac{8}{3} = \tfrac{1}{3} + \left(\tfrac{2}{5} \div \tfrac{8}{3}\right)$$
$$= \tfrac{1}{3} + \left(\tfrac{2}{5} \times \tfrac{3}{8}\right)$$
$$= \tfrac{1}{3} + \tfrac{6}{40}$$
$$= \tfrac{1}{3} + \tfrac{3}{20}$$
$$= \tfrac{20}{60} + \tfrac{9}{60}$$
$$= \tfrac{29}{60}$$

The answer is C.

12. Solution

$$2 + \cfrac{2}{2 + \cfrac{2}{2+2}} = 2 + \cfrac{2}{2 + \frac{2}{4}}$$
$$= 2 + \cfrac{2}{\frac{5}{2}}$$
$$= 2 + \left(\tfrac{2}{5} \times 2\right)$$
$$= 2 + \tfrac{4}{5}$$
$$= 2\tfrac{4}{5}$$

The answer is E.

13. Solution

If $a = 3$ and $b = -1$, the expression $\frac{(a+b)^3}{(a-b)^2}$ has the value $\frac{[3+(-1)]^3}{[3-(-1)]^2} = \frac{2^3}{4^2}$

$$= \tfrac{8}{16}$$
$$= \tfrac{1}{2}$$

The answer is A.

14. Solution

Since $\frac{1}{5} < \frac{n}{40} < \frac{1}{4}$, then $\frac{8}{40} < \frac{n}{40} < \frac{10}{40}$.

Thus, a value for n that satisfies the inequality is $n = 9$.

The answer is B.

15. Solution

The amount of space taken by the 12 letters and the 11 gaps between the letters is $12 \times \frac{3}{5} + 11 \times \frac{1}{5} = \frac{36}{5} + \frac{11}{5} = \frac{47}{5}$ feet.

The amount of space left for the two ends is $15 - \frac{47}{5} = \frac{75}{5} - \frac{47}{5} = \frac{28}{5}$ feet.

Thus, the number of feet left at each of the two ends is $\frac{14}{5}$.

The answer is D.

16. Solution

Since the second rebound is 72 cm, the distance through which the ball dropped to achieve this height was $\frac{3}{2} \times 72 = 108$ cm.

The height of 108 cm represents the height of the first bounce.

Thus, to achieve a first bounce of 108 cm, the ball was originally dropped from a height of $\frac{3}{2} \times 108 = 162$ cm.

The answer is A.

Full Solution Questions

1. Solution 1

$$\begin{aligned} 1 + \frac{3}{10} + \frac{41}{100} &= 1 + 0.3 + 0.41 \\ &= 1.71 \end{aligned}$$

Solution 2

$$\begin{aligned} 1 + \frac{3}{10} + \frac{41}{100} &= 1 + \frac{30}{100} + \frac{41}{100} \\ &= 1 + \frac{71}{100} \\ &= 1.71 \end{aligned}$$

2. Solution

$$\begin{aligned} 1\tfrac{1}{2} + 2\tfrac{2}{3} &= 1\tfrac{3}{6} + 2\tfrac{4}{6} \\ &= 3\tfrac{7}{6} \\ &= 4\tfrac{1}{6} \end{aligned}$$

3. Solution

$$1+\frac{1}{1+\frac{1}{2}}=1+\frac{1}{\frac{3}{2}}=1+\frac{2}{3}=\frac{5}{3}$$

4. Solution

The second fraction is $\frac{11}{12}-\frac{1}{4}=\frac{11}{12}-\frac{3}{12}=\frac{8}{12}=\frac{2}{3}$

5. Solution 1

$\frac{1}{3}$ and half of $\frac{1}{3}$ is $\frac{1}{3}+\left(\frac{1}{2}\times\frac{1}{3}\right)=\frac{1}{3}+\frac{1}{6}=\frac{2}{6}+\frac{1}{6}=\frac{3}{6}=\frac{1}{2}$

Solution 2

$\frac{1}{3}$ and half of $\frac{1}{3}$ is equivalent to one and one half thirds which equals $1\frac{1}{2}\times\frac{1}{3}=\frac{3}{2}\times\frac{1}{3}=\frac{3}{6}=\frac{1}{2}$

6. Solution

Originally there were $30-12=18$ girls in the class.
After the 6 girls join the class, 24 of the 36 students in the class are girls.
The fraction of the class that is female is $\frac{24}{36}=\frac{2}{3}$.

7. Solution

The fraction of the pole that is blue is $1-\frac{1}{3}-\frac{1}{4}=\frac{12}{12}-\frac{4}{12}-\frac{3}{12}=\frac{5}{12}$

8. Solution

After 2 hours have elapsed, the time would be 11:47.
For the last half hour or 30 minutes, 13 minutes would bring the time to 12:00 noon, so that after $2\frac{1}{2}$ hours the time would be 12:17.

9. Solution

$$\frac{2}{3} \div \frac{2}{9} + \frac{1}{2} = \left(\frac{2}{3} \div \frac{2}{9}\right) + \frac{1}{2}$$
$$= \left(\frac{2}{3} \times \frac{9}{2}\right) + \frac{1}{2}$$
$$= \frac{18}{6} + \frac{1}{2}$$
$$= 3\frac{1}{2}$$

10. Solution 1

If $\frac{5}{6}$ of a number is 60, then $\frac{1}{6}$ of the number is $60 \div 5 = 12$.

Thus, the original number is $6 \times 12 = 72$.

Hence, $\frac{3}{4}$ of the original number is $\frac{3}{4} \times 72 = \frac{216}{4} = 54$.

Solution 2

If $\frac{5}{6}$ of a number is 60, then the number is $\frac{6}{5} \times 60 = \frac{360}{5} = 72$.

Hence, $\frac{3}{4}$ of the original number is $\frac{3}{4} \times 72 = \frac{216}{4} = 54$.

11. Solution

$$\left(1 - \frac{1}{2}\right)\left(1 - \frac{1}{3}\right)\left(1 - \frac{1}{4}\right)\left(1 - \frac{1}{5}\right) = \left(\frac{1}{2}\right)\left(\frac{2}{3}\right)\left(\frac{3}{4}\right)\left(\frac{4}{5}\right)$$
$$= \frac{1 \times 2 \times 3 \times 4}{2 \times 3 \times 4 \times 5}$$
$$= \frac{1}{5}$$

12. Solution

The lowest common denominator of the seven fractions is 40.

Now, $\frac{3}{8} = \frac{15}{40}, \frac{4}{5} = \frac{32}{40}, \frac{9}{20} = \frac{18}{40}, \frac{7}{10} = \frac{28}{40}, \frac{1}{2} = \frac{20}{40}$, and $\frac{3}{4} = \frac{30}{40}$.

Of the five given fractions, the only one that is greater than $\frac{1}{2}$ and less than $\frac{3}{4}$ is $\frac{7}{10}$.

13. Solution 1

When $x = \frac{3}{4}$ and $y = \frac{2}{3}$, the expression $\frac{x - y}{x + y}$ has the value

$$\frac{\frac{3}{4} - \frac{2}{3}}{\frac{3}{4} + \frac{2}{3}} = \frac{\frac{9}{12} - \frac{8}{12}}{\frac{9}{12} + \frac{8}{12}}$$
$$= \frac{\frac{1}{12}}{\frac{17}{12}}$$
$$= \frac{1}{12} \times \frac{12}{17}$$
$$= \frac{1}{17}$$

Solution 2

When $x = \frac{3}{4}$ and $y = \frac{2}{3}$, the expression $\frac{x - y}{x + y}$ has the value

$$\begin{aligned}\frac{\frac{3}{4} - \frac{2}{3}}{\frac{3}{4} + \frac{2}{3}} &= \frac{12\left(\frac{3}{4} - \frac{2}{3}\right)}{12\left(\frac{3}{4} + \frac{2}{3}\right)}\\ &= \frac{9 - 8}{9 + 8}\\ &= \frac{1}{17}\end{aligned}$$

14. Solution 1

Since $\frac{1}{3} + \frac{1}{4} + \frac{1}{n} = 1$, then
$$\begin{aligned}\frac{1}{n} &= 1 - \frac{1}{3} - \frac{1}{4}\\ &= 1 - \frac{4}{12} - \frac{3}{12}\\ &= \frac{5}{12}\end{aligned}$$

Thus, $n = \frac{1}{\frac{5}{12}} = \frac{12}{5}$.

Solution 2

Since $\frac{1}{3} + \frac{1}{4} + \frac{1}{n} = 1$, then
$$\begin{aligned}\frac{4}{12} + \frac{3}{12} + \frac{1}{n} &= 1\\ \frac{7}{12} + \frac{1}{n} &= 1\end{aligned}$$

Thus, $\frac{1}{n} = \frac{5}{12}$ and $n = \frac{1}{\frac{5}{12}} = \frac{12}{5}$.

15. Solution

The number of revolutions required to play the song is
$$\begin{aligned}4\tfrac{1}{2} \times 45 &= \frac{9}{2} \times 45\\ &= \frac{405}{2}\\ &= 202\tfrac{1}{2}\end{aligned}$$

At $33\frac{1}{3}$ r.p.m. it still requires $202\frac{1}{2}$ revolutions to play the complete song. It just takes longer to play it (and it won't sound quite the same either).

16. Solution

For a minimum number of tiles, the squares should be as large as possible. The length of each side of the tile must be a number such that $3\frac{3}{5}$ and $4\frac{1}{5}$ are both integral multiples of it.

Since $4\frac{1}{5} = \frac{21}{5} = \frac{1}{5} \times 3 \times 7$ and

$3\frac{3}{5} = \frac{18}{5} = \frac{1}{5} \times 2 \times 3 \times 3$, the largest number

such that $4\frac{1}{5}$ and $3\frac{3}{5}$ are both integral multiples

of it is $\frac{3}{5}$.

The number of $\frac{3}{5} \times \frac{3}{5}$ tiles required to cover the

given rectangle is $7 \times 6 = 42$.

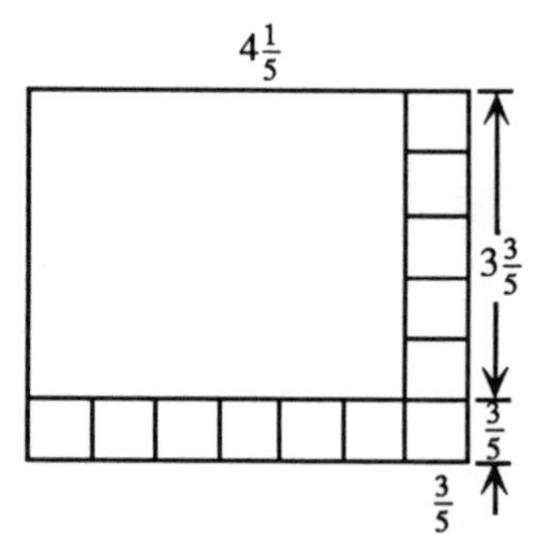

Estimation and Ordering

Multiple Choice Questions

1. Solution

   Each of answers (A), (B), (C), and (D) is true since $(-2)(-3) = 6$ and $6 \geq -9$, $6 \leq 10$, $6 > 0$ and $6 = 6$.
   But $6 \neq -6$, so (E) is false.
   The answer is E.

2. Solution

   299×301 can be approximated as $300 \times 300 = 90\,000$.
   The answer is B.

3. Solution

   The numbers, in order of increasing magnitude, are -25, $-\frac{7}{2}$, -3.1, -3, $-\frac{35}{12}$, -2.
   Since $-\frac{7}{2}$ and -3.1 are not integers, the only integer in the list that is smaller than -3 is -25.
   The answer is D.

4. Solution

   If $m = 1$ and $n = 5$, then $m + n = 1 + 5 = 6$

   $$\frac{m}{n} = \frac{1}{5}$$
   $$n - m = 5 - 1 = 4$$
   $$m \times n = 1 \times 5 = 5$$
   $$m - n = 1 - 5 = -4$$

   Therefore, the expression which has the greatest value is $m + n$.
   The answer is A.

5. Solution

   $\frac{789 \times 97}{0.04}$ can be approximated by evaluating $\frac{800 \times 100}{0.04}$.

   $$\begin{aligned} \frac{800 \times 100}{0.04} &= \frac{80\,000}{0.04} \\ &= \frac{8\,000\,000}{4} \\ &= 2\,000\,000 \end{aligned}$$

   The answer is D.

6. Solution

Jill's yearly gas bill is calculated as $20 \times .48 \times 52$, which can be approximated by $20 \times .50 \times 50 = 500$.

Therefore, Jill's yearly gas bill is approximately \$500.

The answer is C.

7. Solution

$\sqrt[3]{\frac{6.01}{0.099} + 3.95}$ can be approximated by evaluating $\sqrt[3]{\frac{6.00}{0.100} + 4.00}$.

$$\begin{aligned}\sqrt[3]{\frac{6.00}{0.100} + 4.00} &= \sqrt[3]{60 + 4} \\ &= \sqrt[3]{64} \\ &= 4\end{aligned}$$

The answer is A.

8. Solution

The number of seconds in a year is $365 \times 24 \times 60 \times 60$, which can be approximated by evaluating $400 \times 20 \times 60 \times 60$.

$$\begin{aligned}400 \times 20 \times 60 \times 60 &= 8000 \times 3600 \\ &\approx 8000 \times 4000 \\ &= 32\,000\,000 \\ &\approx 30\,000\,000\end{aligned}$$

The answer is A.

9. Solution

The number of people in SSUAG per 850 000 square kilometres is 200 000 000.

The number of people per square kilometre is $\frac{200\,000\,000}{850\,000} = \frac{20\,000}{85}$.

Now, since $\frac{20\,000}{85} \approx \frac{20\,000}{100} = 200$, of the numbers given, the best approximation is 200 people per square kilometre.

The answer is D.

10. Solution

If $x - y > x$, then $y < 0$.

If $y - x < y$, then $x > 0$.

Therefore, $x > y$.

The answer is E.

11. Solution

If $a = 2$ and $b = 3$, then

$$\begin{aligned}\frac{1}{c} &= \frac{1}{a} + \frac{1}{b}\\ &= \frac{1}{2} + \frac{1}{3}\\ &= \frac{3+2}{6}\\ &= \frac{5}{6}\end{aligned}$$

Thus, $c = \frac{6}{5}$, and c is between 1 and 2.

The answer is C.

12. Solution 1

Reversing the digits of the number 77 will not change the sum.

Similarly, reversing the digits of the two numbers 89 and 98 will not change the sum.

Since $47 + 85 = 74 + 58$, the sum is again unaffected.

Thus, Sandy's answer is correct.

Solution 2

We obtain the same answer by showing that

$89 + 98 + 47 + 77 + 85 = 98 + 89 + 74 + 77 + 58 = 396$.

The answer is E.

13. Solution

Let $3x = 5y = 2z = k$, where k is a positive number.

Then, $x = \frac{1}{3}k$, $y = \frac{1}{5}k$, and $z = \frac{1}{2}k$.

Therefore, $y < x < z$.

The answer is B.

14. Solution

If y is a negative integer, then $\frac{13}{24}y < \frac{12}{24}y < \frac{11}{24}y$.

Also, $\frac{11}{20}y < \frac{11}{21}y < \frac{11}{24}y$.

Therefore, $\frac{11}{24}y$ has the greatest value.

The answer is C.

15. Solution

Adding or subtracting a number from both sides of an inequality never changes the sense of the inequality.

Therefore, B and C are always correct.

Multiplying or dividing both sides of an inequality by a positive number never changes the sense of the inequality.

Therefore, D and E are always correct.
Multiplying an inequality by a negative number reverses the sense of the inequality.
Thus, if $z < 0$, (A) is not correct.
The answer is A.

Full Solution Questions

1. Solution
The arrangement, from least to greatest is $-5.5, -0.5, 0$.

2. Solution
The numbers, arranged from least to greatest, are 5.007, 5.018, 5.02, 5.18, 5.2.
Therefore, the middle number is 5.02.

3. Solution 1

$$\begin{aligned}\frac{14}{3}-\frac{2}{5}\times\frac{11}{6} &= \frac{14}{3}-\frac{11}{15}\\ &= \frac{70}{15}-\frac{11}{15}\\ &= \frac{59}{15}\\ &= 3\frac{14}{15}\end{aligned}$$

Therefore, the closest integer is 4.

Solution 2

$$\begin{aligned}\frac{14}{3}-\frac{2}{5}\times\frac{11}{6} &\approx 4.67-0.4\times 1.83\\ &= 4.67-0.732\\ &\approx 3.94\end{aligned}$$

The closest integer is 4.

4. Solution
The numbers in the set, written in order of increasing value, are $-8, \frac{-1}{8}, \frac{1}{8}, 0.8, 1^8$.
The third greatest value is $\frac{1}{8}$.

5. Solution
The numbers in the set, written in order of increasing magnitude, are $-11, -7, -4, \frac{1}{2}, 2$.
Therefore, the sum of the smallest and largest numbers is $-11 + 2 = -9$.

6. Solution

   If $d = 4$, then $2d = 2(4) = 8$

   $-d = -4$

   $-\frac{1}{2}d = -\frac{1}{2}(4) = -2$

   $\frac{16}{d} = \frac{16}{4} = 4$

   $\frac{0}{d} = \frac{0}{4} = 0$

   The numbers, in order from least to greatest, are -4, -2, 0, 4, 8.

   Therefore, the smallest number is $-d = -4$.

7. Solution

   If $d = -5$, then $-3d = -3(-5) = 15$

   $2d = 2(-5) = -10$

   $\frac{15}{d} = \frac{15}{-5} = -3$

   $d^2 = (-5)^2 = 25$

   $\frac{0}{d} = \frac{0}{-5} = 0$

   The numbers, in order from least to greatest, are -10, -3, 0, 15, 25.

   Thus, the smallest number in the set is $2d = -10$.

8. Solution

   There are five equal intervals between 12 and 13.

   Each interval represents a value of $\frac{1}{5}$ or 0.2.

   Thus, the arrow indicates a reading of 12 plus two of these intervals, which is 12.4.

9. Solution

   The five integers, arranged from least to greatest, are $n - 4$, $n - 1$, $n + 3$, $n + 6$, $n + 9$.

   Therefore, the middle integer is $n + 3$.

10. Solution

    The squares of the numbers are 400, $\frac{9}{16}$, 0, $\frac{1}{4}$, and 100, respectively.

    Thus, the only number which is greater than its square is $\frac{1}{2}$.

11. Solution

    The sums of the groups in succession are 15, 40, 65, 90, 115, 140, 165, ...

    The sixth row has a sum nearest to 150.

12. Solution

The maximum value of $\frac{y}{x}$ occurs when y takes on its largest value and x takes on its smallest value.

The maximum value of $\frac{y}{x}$ is $\frac{40}{4} = 10$.

The minimum value of $\frac{y}{x}$ occurs when y takes on its smallest value and x takes on its largest value.

The minimum value of $\frac{y}{x}$ is $\frac{20}{8} = \frac{5}{2}$.

13. Solution

We are given that $0 < x < 1$ and $y \geq 1$.

Thus, (i) $\frac{x}{y} \leq x < 1$.

(ii) $\frac{1}{x} > 1$, since $0 < x < 1$, and so $\left(\frac{1}{x}\right)(y) = \frac{y}{x} > y$ where $y \geq 1$.

(iii) $x^y \leq x < 1$, since an integral power of a number less than 1 results in a smaller number $\left[\text{e.g., } \left(\frac{1}{2}\right)^3 = \frac{1}{8}\right]$.

(iv) $y - x < y$.

(v) $xy < y$ since $x < 1$.

Of the expressions given, $\frac{y}{x}$ has the largest value.

Area and Perimeter

Multiple Choice Questions

1. Solution 1

   Since the missing lengths are each 4 cm, the perimeter is
   $12 + 10 + 4 + 6 + 8 + 4 = 44$ cm.

   Solution 2

   A more elegant solution is obtained by realizing that the perimeter of the given figure is the same as that of a rectangle having width 10 and length 12.
   Hence, the perimeter is $2(10 + 12) = 2(22) = 44$ cm.
   The answer is B.

2. Solution

   The area of a triangle may be calculated by using the formula $A = \frac{1}{2}(\text{base} \times \text{altitude})$.
   $BC = 5$ cm may be used as a base and $AD = 4$ cm may be used as an altitude.
   The area of triangle ABC is $A = \frac{1}{2}(5)(4) = 10\ \text{cm}^2$.
   The answer is E.

3. Solution

   The area of rectangle $ABCD$ is $AD \times AB$.
   Therefore, $12 \times AB = 60$
   $AB = 5$
   The length of AB is 5 cm.
   The answer is A.

4. Solution

   The perimeter of each of the figures A, B, C, and E is 10 units.
   The perimeter of figure D is 12 units.
   Hence, figure D has the greatest perimeter.
   The answer is D.

5. Solution

   The shaded area is the area of the larger square minus the area of the smaller square.
   Therefore, the area is $y^2 - x^2$.
   The answer is D.

6. Solution

The unshaded triangle and the rectangle have the same base and the same height. Hence, the area of that triangle is one-half the area of the rectangle.
But the shaded area is the other half of the rectangle.
Therefore, the shaded area is $\frac{1}{2}(11)(7) = \frac{77}{2}$.
The answer is A.

7. Solution

The area of the figure is the same as the area of five identical squares, each of side 2 cm.
The area of each square is $2 \times 2 = 4$ cm^2.
The area of the given figure is $5 \times 4 = 20$ cm^2.
The answer is C.

8. Solution

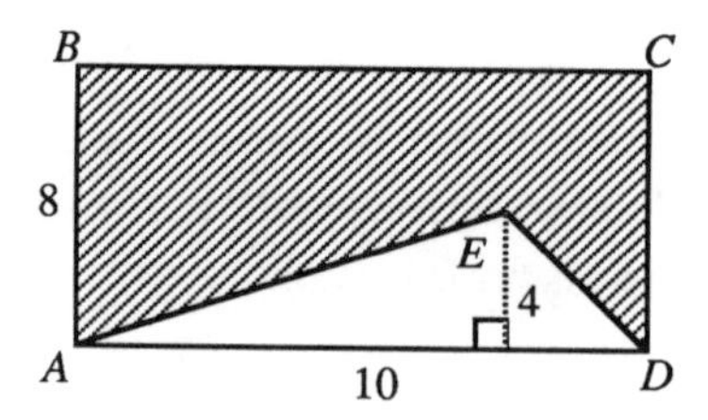

The shaded area is the area of rectangle *ABCD* minus the area of triangle *ADE*.
The area of rectangle *ABCD* is
$8 \times 10 = 80$ cm^2.
The area of triangle *ADE* is
$\frac{1}{2} \times 10 \times 4 = 20$ cm^2.
Therefore, the shaded area is $80 - 20 = 60$ cm^2.
The answer is C.

9. Solution 1

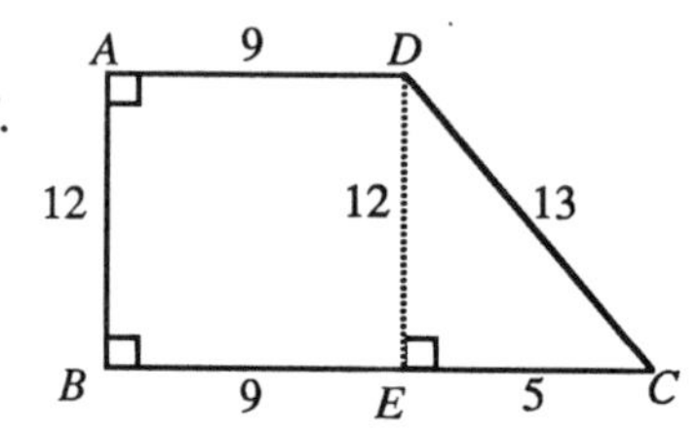

The area of figure *ABCD* equals the area of rectangle *ABED* plus the area of triangle *DEC*.
The area is $12 \times 9 + \frac{1}{2}(12)(5) = 108 + 30$
$= 138$ m^2

Solution 2

Since *AD* is parallel to *BC*, the figure *ABCD* is a trapezoid.
The area of a trapezoid is one-half the sum of the parallel sides times the perpendicular distance between them.

Hence, the area of $ABCD = \frac{1}{2}(AD + BC)(AB)$

$$= \frac{1}{2}(9 + 14)(12)$$
$$= \frac{1}{2}(23)(12)$$
$$= 138 \text{ m}^2$$

The answer is B.

10. Solution 1

The area formed by the sidewalk and the garden is a rectangle with dimensions 12 m by 22 m.

The area of the sidewalk is the area of the large rectangle minus the area of the garden.

The area is

$(12 \times 22) - (10 \times 20) = 264 - 200 = 64 \text{ m}^2$.

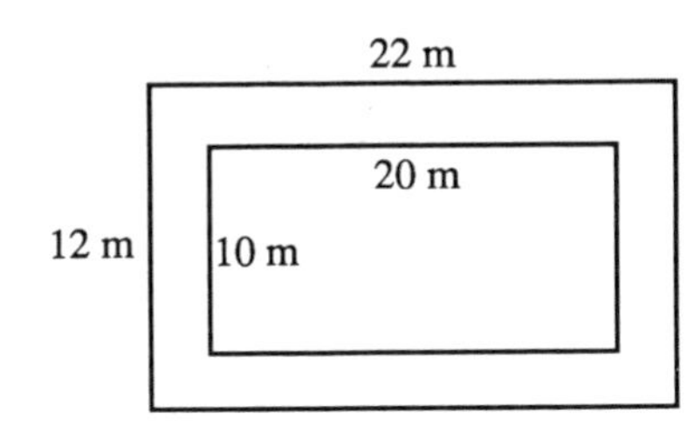

Solution 2

The area of the sidewalk may be considered as four rectangles, one along each edge of the garden, plus the four squares at the corners.

The total area is

$(10)(1) + (20)(1) + (10)(1) + 20(1) + 4(1)(1)$

$= 10 + 20 + 10 + 20 + 4$

$= 64 \text{ m}^2$

The answer is D.

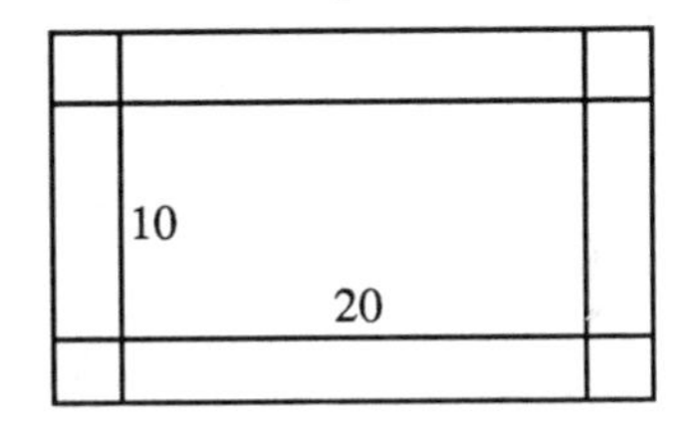

11. Solution 1

Since the two squares have areas of 4 cm^2 and 9 cm^2, the sides of the two squares are 2 cm and 3 cm, respectively.

Therefore, the dimensions of each of the rectangles is 2 cm by 3 cm.

Therefore, the total shaded area is $3 \times 2 + 2 \times 3 = 12 \text{ cm}^2$.

Solution 2

Since the two squares have areas of 4 cm^2 and 9 cm^2, the sides of the two smaller squares are 2 cm and 3 cm, respectively.

Therefore, the side of the square *ABCD* is 5 cm.

The shaded area is the area of square *ABCD* minus the sum of the areas of the two smaller squares.

Thus, the shaded area is $5^2 - (4 + 9) = 25 - 13$

$$= 12 \text{ cm}^2$$

The answer is B.

12. Solution

An isosceles triangle has two equal sides.
If two of the sides have lengths 10 cm and 3 cm, the only possibilities for the length of the third side are 3 cm and 10 cm.
In order to form a triangle, the sum of the lengths of any two sides must be greater than the length of the third side.
Consequently, 3 cm cannot be the length of the third side.
Thus, the perimeter is $10 + 10 + 3 = 23$ cm.
The answer is C.

13. Solution 1

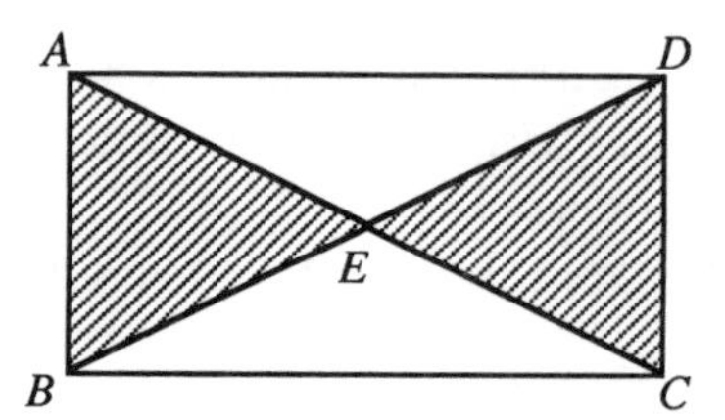

The vertex, E, of the shaded triangles, because of symmetry, must be equidistant from AB and DC.
Therefore, the distance from E to AB or to DC is 4.
Each shaded triangle has a base of 6 and a height
of 4.
Therefore, each triangle has area $\frac{1}{2} \times 6 \times 4 = 12$.
The total shaded area is $12 + 12 = 24$.

Solution 2

Since the area of the rectangle is $8 \times 6 = 48$, and it contains 4 equal triangles, each triangle has an area of $\frac{48}{4} = 12$.
The shaded area is $12 + 12 = 24$.
The answer is E.

14. Solution 1

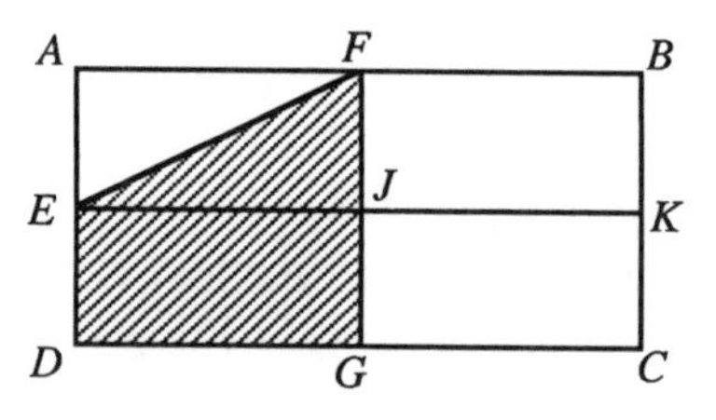

In the diagram $AFGD$ and $FBCG$ are equal squares.
If E is joined to K, the midpoint of BC, then EJK cuts each square into equal parts.
Hence, triangle FEJ is $\frac{1}{2}$ of rectangle $AFJE$ or $\frac{1}{4}$ of square $AFGD$.
Thus, the shaded area $EFGD$ is $\frac{3}{4}$ of square $AFGD$, or $\frac{1}{2}$ of $\frac{3}{4}$ of rectangle $ABCD$.
Thus, the ratio of the shaded area to the area of $ABCD$ is $\frac{3}{8}$.

Solution 2

Partition the given figure by drawing in the line segments as shown in the diagram.

This creates eight identical triangles, three of which are shaded.

The ratio of the shaded area to the entire figure is $\frac{3}{8}$.

The answer is E.

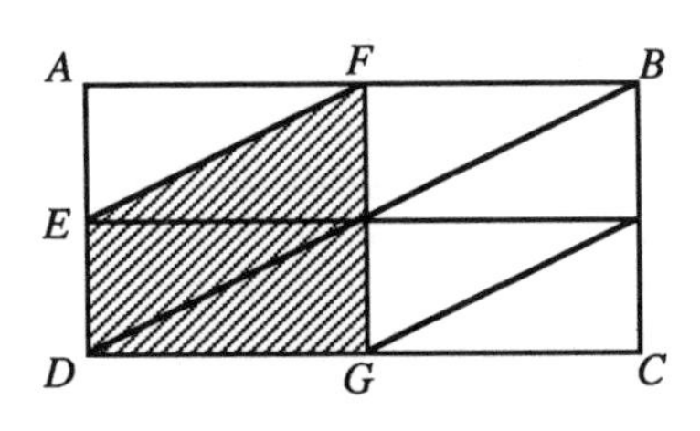

15. Solution

The side of the first square is x cm, so its perimeter is $4x$ cm.

The side of the second square is $(2x + 1)$ cm, so its perimeter is $4(2x + 1) = (8x + 4)$ cm.

The total perimeter is
$$4x + 8x + 4 = 100$$
$$12x + 4 = 100$$
$$12x = 96$$
$$x = 8$$

The length of the side of the larger square is $2x + 1 = 2(8) + 1 = 17$ cm.

The answer is B.

16. Solution

The area of a triangle may be expressed by the formula $A = \frac{1}{2}$ base $\times$ height.

Since any side of a triangle may be used as the base,

then
$$\tfrac{1}{2}(BC)(AD) = \tfrac{1}{2}(AC)(BE)$$
$$\tfrac{1}{2}(6)(2) = \tfrac{1}{2}(4)(BE)$$
$$6 = 2BE$$
$$BE = \tfrac{6}{2} = 3$$

The answer is C.

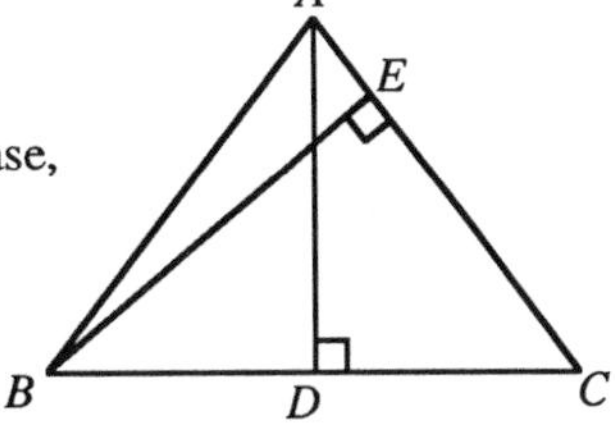

Full Solution Questions

1. Solution

Let the width of the room be w feet.

Then, the length of the room is $(w + 7)$ feet.

The perimeter is
$$w + (w + 7) + w + (w + 7) = 34$$
$$4w + 14 = 34$$
$$4w = 20$$
$$w = 5$$

The length of the room is $5 + 7 = 12$ feet.

2. Solution 1

By comparing the lengths of opposite sides, the missing lengths of the segments are 17 m and 29 m.

The perimeter is $30 + 20 + 13 + 17 + 10 + 3 + 29 + 10 + 4 + 30 = 166$ m.

Solution 2

The perimeter of the warehouse is the same as the perimeter of the 40 by 43 rectangle illustrated,

i.e., $(40 + 43) \times 2 = 166$ m.

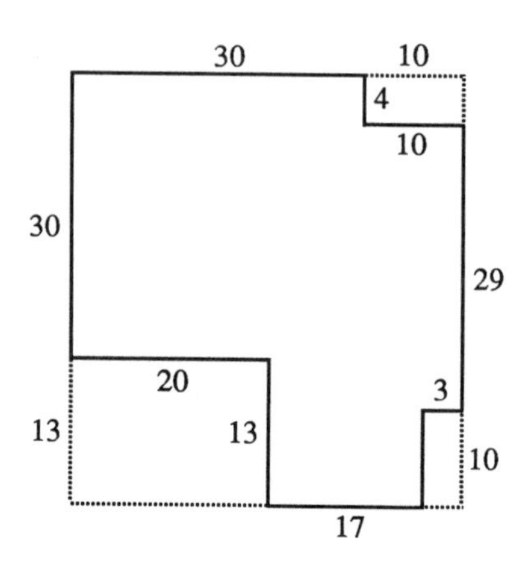

3. Solution 1

If a perpendicular is drawn from B to DC meeting DC at E, the figure is divided into rectangle $ADEB$ and triangle BEC.

The area of $ADEB$ is $4 \times 3 = 12$ square units.

The area of BEC is $\frac{1}{2}(EC)(BE) = \frac{1}{2}(2)(3) = 3$ square units.

The area of figure $ABCD$ is $12 + 3 = 15$ square units.

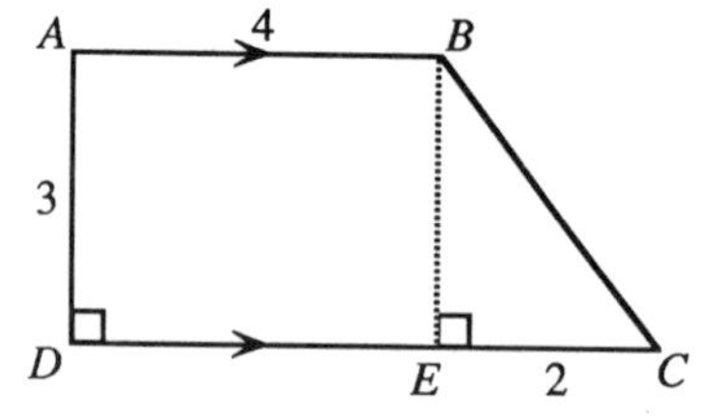

Solution 2

A figure with two of its opposite sides parallel is called a trapezoid.

The area of a trapezoid is equal to the product of one-half the sum of the parallel sides multiplied

by the perpendicular distance between them.

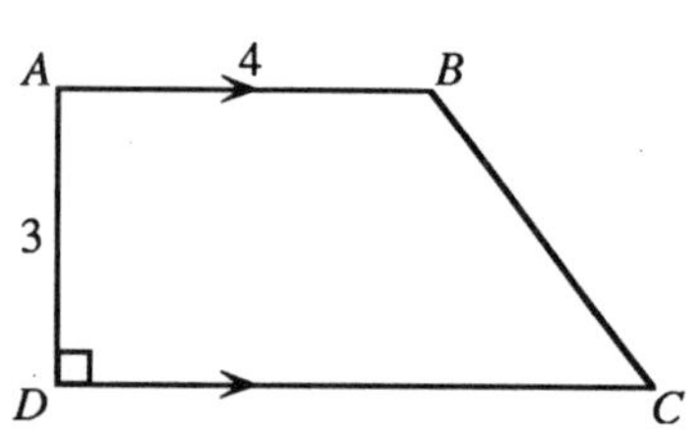

The area of trapezoid $ABCD$ is $\frac{1}{2}(AB + DC)(AD)$

$$= \frac{1}{2}(4 + 6)(3)$$

$$= \frac{1}{2}(10)(3)$$

$$= 15 \text{ square units}$$

4. Solution

The sum of the horizontal line segments is the same as the distance across the bottom of the pile, i.e., $4 \times 8 = 32$ cm.

The sum of the vertical line segments is $8 \times 2 = 16$ cm.

The total length of the path is $32 + 16 = 48$ cm.

5. Solution

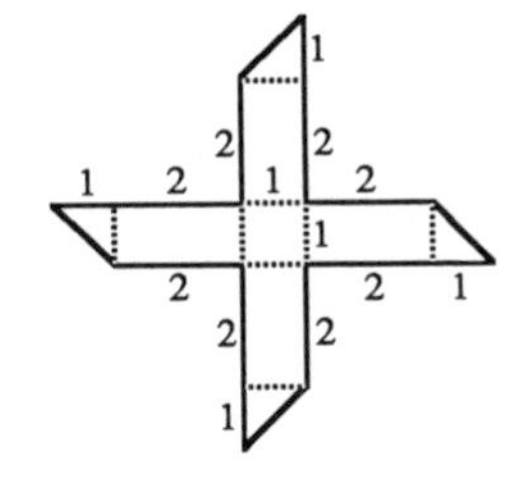

There are many ways of partitioning the given figure to find the area.

If the partitioning is done as shown in the diagram, the original figure is composed of four 2×1 rectangles, a 1×1 square, and four triangles that can be used to form two 1×1 squares.

The area is $4(2 \times 1) + 1 + 2 = 11$ square units.

6. Solution

Since the perimeter of the rectangle is 64 cm, one-half of the perimeter is 32 cm.

Since the length is 20 cm, the width is $32 - 20 = 12$ cm.

The area is $20 \times 12 = 240$ cm^2.

7. Solution

The area of the square is $20 \times 20 = 400$ cm^2.

The area of the circle is $\pi r^2 = \frac{22}{7}(7)^2 = \frac{22}{7} \times 7 \times 7 = 154$ cm^2.

The area of the square not covered by the circle is $400 - 154 = 246$ cm^2.

8. Solution 1

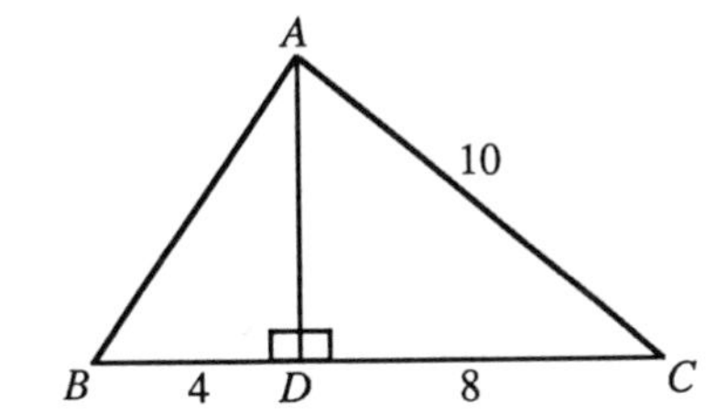

The area of triangle ADC is $\frac{1}{2}(8)(AD) = 24$.

Therefore, $AD = 6$.

The area of triangle ABD is $\frac{1}{2}(BD)(AD)$

$= \frac{1}{2}(4)(6)$

$= 12$ square units

Solution 2

Triangle ABD has the same height as triangle ADC, but its base is only one-half the base of triangle ADC.

Therefore, the area of triangle ABD is one-half the area of triangle ADC.

The area of triangle ABD is $\frac{1}{2}(24) = 12$ square units.

9. Solution

The two circles are equal, and touch each other and the sides of the rectangle, as shown.
Since the distance between their centres is 8 cm, each circle has radius 4 cm.
The length and width of the rectangle are 16 cm and 8 cm, respectively.
The area of the rectangle is $16 \times 8 = 128$ cm^2.

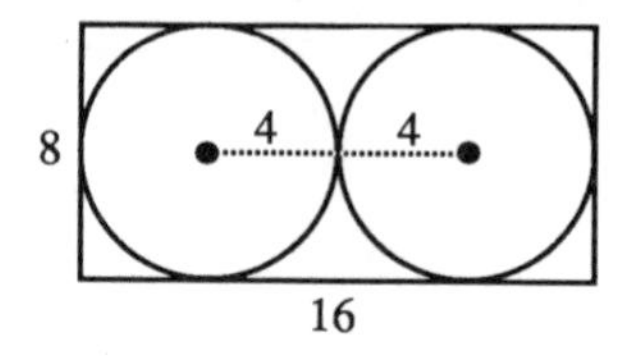

10. Solution

The diagonal of a rectangle divides it into two congruent triangles.
Since the area of one triangle is 6.5 m^2, then the area of the rectangle is $2(6.5) = 13$ m^2.
In a rectangle, the area is equal to the product of the length and width, and since the area is 13, the sides must be of length 13 and 1. These are the only positive integer divisors of 13.
The perimeter is $13 + 1 + 13 + 1 = 28$ metres.

11. Solution

The perimeter is equal to the circumference of the semicircle *AED* plus the lengths of the line segments *AB*, *BC*, and *CD*.
The circumference of semicircle *AED* is $\frac{1}{2}(\pi)(4) = 2\pi$.
To find the length of *BC*, draw *BF*, as shown in the diagram.
In triangle *BFC*, $BF = AD = 4$ and $FC = CD - DF = 9 - 6 = 3$.
Using the Pythagorean Theorem,

$$\begin{aligned}(BC)^2 &= (BF)^2 + (FC)^2 \\ &= 4^2 + 3^2 \\ &= 25 \\ BC &= 5\end{aligned}$$

The perimeter of the figure is $2\pi + 6 + 5 + 9 = 20 + 2\pi$.

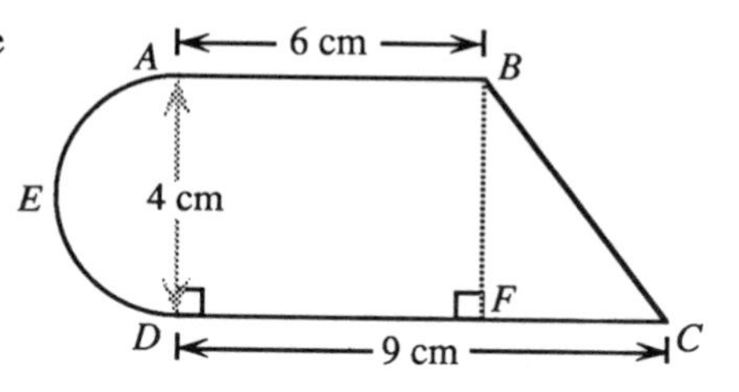

12. Solution

Using *CD* as height and *AB* as base, the area of ΔABC is

$$\begin{aligned}\tfrac{1}{2}(AB)(CD) = \tfrac{1}{2}(AB)(6) &= 48 \\ 3AB &= 48 \\ AB &= 16\end{aligned}$$

Using BE as height and AC as base, the area of ΔABC is

$$\tfrac{1}{2}(AC)(BE) = \tfrac{1}{2}(AC)(8) = 48$$
$$4AC = 48$$
$$AC = 12$$

Therefore, $AB + AC = 16 + 12 = 28$ units.

13. Solution 1

Because of the Pythagorean Theorem, a triangle with sides 3, 4, and 5 is right-angled. This confirms the area is $\frac{1}{2}(3)(4) = 6$ square inches.

The new triangle has sides which are $3 \times 3 = 9$, $3 \times 4 = 12$, and $3 \times 5 = 15$ inches, respectively.

This triangle is also right-angled.

Its area is $\frac{1}{2}(9)(12) = 54$ square inches.

Solution 2

Let the area of the original triangle be A square inches.

If the sides of the original triangle are doubled, the area becomes $2^2A = 4A$.

If the sides of the original triangle are multiplied by 3, the area becomes $3^2A = 9A$.

Since the original area was 6 square inches, the new area is $9(6) = 54$ square inches.

14. Solution

The segment RS may be used as a side of square $QRST$ and as a base of triangle PRS. Since the area of square $QRST$ equals the area of triangle PRS, then

$(RS)^2 = \frac{1}{2}(RS)(PR)$.

Therefore, $(12)(12) = \frac{1}{2}(12)(PR)$

$$144 = 6PR$$
$$PR = 24$$

The length of PR is 24.

15. Solution

Let the sides of the two new squares be a cm and b cm.

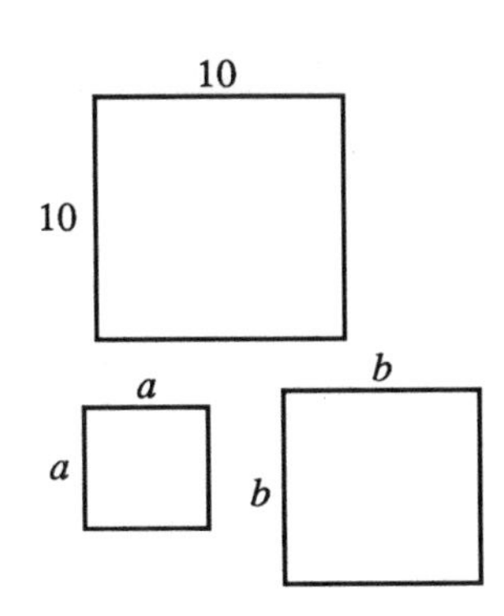

The area of the given square is 100 cm^2, the sum of the areas of the two smaller squares equals 100 cm^2.

Thus, $a^2 + b^2 = 100$.

Since a and b are integers, a^2 and b^2 are perfect squares.

By checking the squares of the integers from 1 to 10, we discover the only solution is
$6^2 + 8^2 = 100$.
The total perimeter of the two new squares is
$4(6) + 4(8) = 24 + 32 = 56$ cm.

16. Solution 1

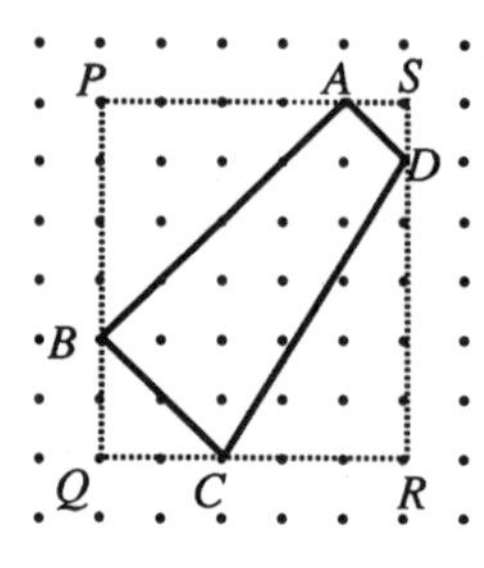

The area of *ABCD* equals the area of rectangle *PQRS* minus the sum of the areas of triangles *PAB*, *ASD*, *BQC*, and *DCR*.
The area of *ABCD* is
$6 \times 5 - \left(\frac{1}{2} \times 4 \times 4 + \frac{1}{2} \times 1 \times 1 + \frac{1}{2} \times 2 \times 2 + \frac{1}{2} \times 3 \times 5\right)$
$= 30 - \left(8 + \frac{1}{2} + 2 + \frac{15}{2}\right)$
$= 30 - 18$
$= 12$

Solution 2

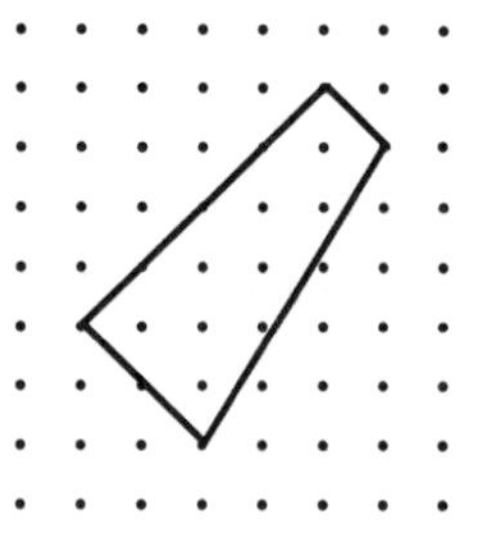

Pick's Theorem states that the area of a polygon P with lattice points as vertices is given by

$$A = \frac{1}{2}e + i - 1$$

where e is the number of lattice points lying on the edges of P and i is the number of lattice points lying inside P.
Therefore, the area of *ABCD* is $\frac{1}{2}(8) + 9 - 1 = 12$.

Solution 3

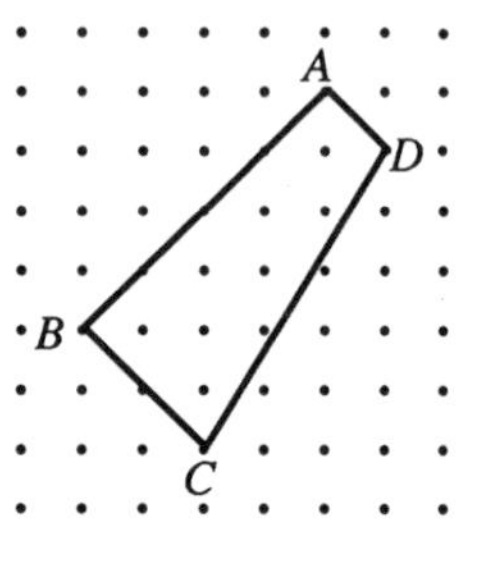

Since *AD* and *BC* are parallel, *ABCD* is a trapezoid.
In addition, *AB* is perpendicular to *BC*.
Using the Pythagoream Theorem, the lengths of *AB*, *AD*, and *BC* are $4\sqrt{2}$, $\sqrt{2}$, and $2\sqrt{2}$, respectively.
Therefore, the area of $ABCD = \frac{1}{2}(AD + BC)AB$
$= \frac{1}{2}(\sqrt{2} + 2\sqrt{2})4\sqrt{2}$
$= \frac{1}{2} \times 3\sqrt{2} \times 4\sqrt{2}$
$= 6 \times 2$
$= 12$

Percentages - II

Multiple Choice Questions

1. Solution

   20% of $20 = \frac{20}{100} \times 20$
   $= 4$

   The answer is E.

2. Solution

   $\frac{1}{10}$ of $1\% = \frac{1}{10} \times \frac{1}{100}$
   $= \frac{1}{1000}$
   $= 0.001$

   The answer is D.

3. Solution

   115% of $15 = 1.15 \times 15$
   $= 17.25$

   The nearest whole number is 17.
   The answer is C.

4. Solution 1

   If 2% of a number is 8, then 1% of the number is 4.
   Thus, 100% of the number is 400.

   Solution 2

   Let the number be x.
   Then, $\frac{2}{100}x = 8$.
   Hence, $x = 50(8) = 400$.
   The answer is D.

5. Solution

   The failure rate is $\frac{3}{16} \times 100\% = 18\frac{3}{4}\%$.
   The answer is A.

6. Solution
   The approximate number of Canadians with Type O blood is
   $\frac{46}{100} \times 25\,000\,000 = 11\,500\,000$.
   The answer is B.

7. Solution 1
   The reduction is $\frac{35}{100} \times \$25.00 = \$8.75$.
   The sale price is $\$25.00 - \$8.75 = \$16.25$.

   Solution 2
   If the reduction is 35 percent of the original price, then the sale price is 65 percent of the original price.
   Thus, the sale price is $\frac{65}{100} \times \$25.00 = \$16.25$.
   The answer is C.

8. Solution 1
   The original price was \$85.50.
   The reduction is 10% of $\$85.50 = \frac{10}{100}(\$85.50) = \$8.55$.
   Thus, the selling price is $\$85.50 - \$8.55 = \$76.95$.

   Solution 2
   The selling price is 90% of the original price.
   Thus, the selling price is $\frac{90}{100}(\$85.50) = \$76.95$.
   The answer is D.

9. Solution
   Let the original price of the article be p.
   The reduced price is 80% of $p = \frac{4}{5}p$.
   To restore the value $\frac{4}{5}p$ to p, it must be multiplied by $\frac{5}{4}$.
   As a percent, $\frac{5}{4} = \frac{125}{100} = 125\%$.
   Thus, the reduced price must be increased by 25% to restore the original price.
   The answer is C.

10. Solution
    If Frank earns 6% more than Bob, then Frank earns 106% of Bob's salary.
    Thus, Frank earns $\frac{106}{100}(\$25\,000) = \$26\,500$.
    The answer is A.

11. Solution

The number of students wearing glasses is 40% of 30 = $0.4 \times 30 = 12$.
Of these, $\frac{3}{12} = \frac{1}{4}$ or 25% are left-handed.
The answer is B.

12. Solution

The number of points scored by Pierre is 125% of the number scored by Jim.
If Jim scored x points, then

$$\begin{aligned}\frac{125}{100}x &= 220\\ \frac{5}{4}x &= 220\\ x &= \frac{4}{5}(220)\\ &= 176\end{aligned}$$

Thus, Jim scored 176 points.
The answer is D.

13. Solution

The total number of votes cast was $10\,575 + 7990 + 2585 = 21\,150$.
This number represents 90% of the total.
If the total number of voters was x, then

$$\begin{aligned}\frac{90}{100}x &= 21\,150\\ 0.9x &= 21\,150\\ x &= \frac{21150}{0.9}\\ &= 23\,500\end{aligned}$$

The answer is E.

14. Solution 1

The cost of twenty Gauss Contest Problem Books at \$10.00 each is $20 \times \$10 = \$200$.
The Goods and Services Tax is 7% of \$200 = $\frac{7}{100} \times \$200 = \$14.00$.
The total cost of the books is \$200 + \$14 = \$214.00.

Solution 2

The cost of a single book with tax included is 107% of \$10.00 = \$10.70.
The total cost of 20 books is $20 \times \$10.70 = \$214.00$.
The answer is B.

15. Solution 1

$\frac{0.33}{0.11} = \frac{3}{1} = \frac{300}{100} = 300\%$.

Solution 2

$\frac{0.33}{0.11}$ of 100% = 3(100%) = 300%.
The answer is D.

16. Solution

Let the costs of the two pipes be p_1 and p_2 dollars.

Then, $\frac{120}{100}p_1 = \$1.20$

$p_1 = \$1.00$

and $\frac{80}{100}p_2 = \$1.20$

$p_2 = \$1.50$

Thus, he made a profit of 20 cents on one pipe and a loss of 30 cents on the other pipe, resulting in a net loss of 10 cents on the transaction.

The answer is D.

Full Solution Questions

1. Solution 1

$$\frac{2}{3}\% \text{ of } 600 = \frac{\frac{2}{3}}{100} \times 600 = \frac{2}{3} \times 6 = 4$$

Solution 2

$$1\% \text{ of } 600 = \frac{1}{100} \times 600 = 6$$

Therefore, $\frac{2}{3}\%$ of $600 = \frac{2}{3} \times 6 = 4$

2. Solution

$$200\% \text{ of } 20 = \frac{200}{100} \times 20 = 40$$

Thus, 20 increased by 200% of itself is $20 + 40 = 60$.

3. Solution

The sale price is 70% of $\$7.00 = 0.7 \times \$7.00 = \$4.90$.

4. Solution

The reduced price for the drill is $\frac{90}{100} \times \$14.00 = \$12.60$.

The sales tax is $\frac{7}{100} \times \$12.60 = \$0.88$.

Joe would pay a total price of $\$12.60 + \$0.88 = \$13.48$.

5. Solution

The team will play a total of $75 + 45 = 120$ games.

For a winning percentage of 60%, it must win a total of $0.6 \times 120 = 72$ games.

Since the team has already won 50 games, it must win 22 of its remaining 45 games.

6. Solution

The price after successive reductions of 20% and 10% was $(0.9)[(0.8)(\$55)] = \$39.60$.

The total reduction was $\$55.00 - \$39.60 = \$15.40$.

7. Solution

$x = \frac{3}{100}y = 0.03y$

$y = \frac{7}{100}w = 0.07w$

Thus, $x = (0.03)(0.07w) = 0.0021w$.

8. Solution 1

The 1987 price for one kilogram of Schwartz' cheese was \$12.00.

The 1988 price was 110% of \$12.00 which equals $1.1 \times \$12.00 = \$13.20$ per kg.

The 1989 price was 110% of \$13.20 which equals $1.1 \times \$13.20 = \$14.52$ per kg.

Solution 2

The 1989 price was 110% of the 1988 price which equals 110% of 110% of the 1987 price.

Thus, the 1989 price was $(1.1)[(1.1)(\$12.00)] = \$14.52$ per kg.

9. Solution

The value of 30 American dollars is $\frac{130}{100} \times \$30 = 1.30 \times \$30$

$= 39$ Canadian dollars.

Thus, the tourist's change, in Canadian dollars, should be $\$39.00 - \$35.00 = \$4.00$.

10. Solution

The sale price (without tax) is 70% of \$16.00 which is $\frac{70}{100} \times \$16.00 = \$11.20$.

The sales tax is 7% of the amount paid which is 7% of $\$11.20 = \frac{7}{100} \times \$11.20 = \$0.78$.

The amount you would pay is $\$11.20 + \$0.78 = \$11.98$.

11. Solution

The reduction is 20% of $\$100 = \$20$, so the sale price is $\$100 - \$20 = \$80$.

In order to restore the price to \$100 an amount of \$20 is needed.

The percentage increase from the \$80 price is $\frac{20}{80} = \frac{1}{4} = 25\%$.

12. Solution

Let the original length and width be l and w, respectively.

The new dimensions are $1.15l$ and $0.8w$.

The new area is $(1.15l)(0.8w) = 0.92lw$

$= 92\%$ of lw

Thus, the new area is 8% less than the original area.

13. Solution

For the first 50 units produced, the worker earned $50 \times \$0.70 = \$35$.

For the next 30 units produced, the worker earned $30 \times \$0.80 = \$24$.

Since the worker earned \$86 in a day, he must have earned $\$86 - (\$35 + \$24) = \$27$ at the 90 cent rate.

To earn \$27 at a rate of 90 cents per unit, the worker must have produced $\$27 \div \$0.9 = 30$ units.

The number of units produced was $50 + 30 + 30 = 110$.

14. Solution

To have a winning percentage of 60%, the ratio of wins to losses must be 60:40 or 3:2.

Since the team has lost 30 games, it must win 15 successive games so that the ratio of wins to losses becomes 45:30 or 3:2.

Thus, 15 successive wins will raise its winning percentage from 50% to 60%.

15. Solution

Since 40% of the cars contained two or more people, then 60% of the cars contained only one person.

The percentage of all cars containing only one male is

25% of $60\% = \frac{25}{100}$ of $60\% = 15\%$.

Since 40% of the cars contained two or more people, and 15% contained exactly one male, then the percentage of cars containing exactly one female is

$[100 - (40 + 15)] = 45$.

Divisibility and Factoring

Multiple Choice Questions

1. Solution

$5 = 5$

$10 = 2 \times 5$

$35 = 5 \times 7$

The L.C.M. is $5 \times 2 \times 7 = 70$.

The H.C.F. is 5.

The difference between the L.C.M. and the H.C.F. is 65.

The answer is A.

2. Solution

Since $105 = 3 \times 5 \times 7$, the divisors of 105, excluding 1 and 105, are 3, 5, 7, 3×5, 3×7, and 5×7.

There are six divisors.

The answer is B.

3. Solution

Since $2^{10} - 1$ is odd, it cannot be divisible by 2, 4, 8, or 10. The only possible divisor in the list is 3.

The answer is C.

4. Solution

$(2^7 - 2) \div 7 = (128 - 2) \div 7 = 18$

$(2^5 - 2) \div 5 = (32 - 2) \div 5 = 6$

The sum of the quotients is $18 + 6 = 24$.

The answer is C.

5. Solution

$180 = 2 \times 2 \times 3 \times 3 \times 5$

$320 = 2 \times 2 \times 2 \times 2 \times 2 \times 2 \times 5$

$360 = 2 \times 2 \times 2 \times 3 \times 3 \times 5$

$420 = 2 \times 2 \times 3 \times 5 \times 7$

$540 = 2 \times 2 \times 3 \times 3 \times 3 \times 5$

To be a multiple of 15, the number must contain factors 3 and 5; hence 180, 360, 420, and 540 are all multiples of 15.
To be a multiple of 18, the number must contain factors 2, 3, and 3; hence 320 and 420 are not multiples of 18.
Therefore, 420 is a multiple of 15 but not of 18.
The answer is D.

6. Solution
   To be divisible by 6, a number must be divisible by 2 and hence it must be even.
   Using the given digits, the only two even numbers possible are 132 and 312.
   Both of these are divisible by 6.
   The answer is A.

7. Solution
   To solve this problem we first find the number of zeros at the end of the integer N.
   Zeros are obtained when we take the product of multiples of 10 and also when we take the product of multiples of 5 and even integers.
   Thus, we obtain four zeros at the end of N when we use the factors 20, 10, 15, and 5.
   Since 90 000 has four zeros at the end, it is the largest of the given integers that divides N exactly.
   The answer is C.

8. Solution
   Since $60K = 2^2 \times 3 \times 5 \times K$ and each prime factor of a perfect square must occur an even number of times, the smallest value of K is $3 \times 5 = 15$.
   The answer is B.

9. Solution
   The second perfect number is 28 since $28 = 1 + 2 + 4 + 7 + 14$.
   The answer is A.

10. Solution
    The shaded area contains the odd multiples of 7 from 1 to 50, namely the four numbers 7, 21, 35, and 49.
    The answer is C.

11. Solution 1

The sets of positive integers that leave remainders 1, 4, and 1 when divided by 3, 5, and 11 respectively, are

$S_1 = \{1, 4, 7, 10, 13, 16, 19, 22, 25, 28, 31, 34, 37, ...\}$

$S_2 = \{4, 9, 14, 19, 24, 29, 34, 39, 44, ...\}$

$S_3 = \{1, 12, 23, 34, 45, ...\}$

The least integer common to S_1, S_2, and S_3 is 34.

Solution 2

The least positive integer that is divisible by both 3 and 11 is 33. Therefore 34 leaves remainder 1 on division by either 3 or 11. But 34 also leaves remainder 4 on division by 5.

Hence, 34 is the required integer.

The answer is C.

12. Solution

If n is odd, $n(n + 2)(n + 4)$ is the product of three consecutive odd integers.

If n is even, $n(n + 2)(n + 4)$ is the product of three consecutive even integers.

In either case, one of the integers will be a multiple of 3.

Therefore, $n(n + 2)(n + 4)$ is always divisible by 3.

The answer is C.

13. Solution 1

Let the number of revolutions that wheel B must turn be b.

This will cause wheel A to turn by $21b$ teeth.

In order that wheel A end up in its starting position, $21b$ must be a multiple of 35.

The smallest value of b to satisfy this condition is 5.

Solution 2

In order that the wheels return to their starting positions, both must turn an integral number of revolutions.

Let the number of revolutions of wheel A be a and of wheel B be b.

Thus, $35a = 21b$.

Since $35a$ must be a multiple of 21 and $21b$ must be a multiple of 35, we require the least common multiple of 21 and 35, which is 105.

Therefore, $a = 3$ and $b = 5$.

Hence, B must turn 5 revolutions before the wheels return to their starting position.

The answer is B.

14. Solution

Since the lowest common multiple of 12 and 20 is 60, buses will leave together every 60 minutes.

Since they leave together at 1:00 p.m., another time they will leave together is 3:00 p.m.

The answer is D.

Full Solution Questions

1. Solution

Since $12 = 2 \times 2 \times 3$, $20 = 2 \times 2 \times 5$, and $36 = 2 \times 2 \times 3 \times 3$, the highest common factor of the three integers is $2 \times 2 = 4$.

2. Solution

$4 = 2 \times 2$

$20 = 2 \times 2 \times 5$

$28 = 2 \times 2 \times 7$

The H.C.F. is $2 \times 2 = 4$.

The L.C.M. is $2 \times 2 \times 5 \times 7 = 140$.

The sum of the H.C.F. and L.C.M. is 144.

3. Solution

Since $24 = 2^3 \times 3$, the divisors of 24 are 1, 2, 2^2, 2^3, 3, 2×3, $2^2 \times 3$, and $2^3 \times 3$.

The sum of the divisors is $1 + 2 + 4 + 8 + 3 + 6 + 12 + 24 = 60$.

4. Solution

The set of all prime numbers greater than 6 and less than 37 is $\{7, 11, 13, 17, 19, 23, 29, 31\}$.

5. Solution 1

$$\begin{aligned} 45 \times 45 \times N &= 45 \times 2 \times 45 \times 2 \times 45 \times 2 \\ &= 45 \times 45 \times (2 \times 2 \times 2 \times 45) \\ &= 45 \times 45 \times 360 \end{aligned}$$

Therefore, $N = 360$.

Solution 2

$$\begin{aligned} N &= \frac{90 \times 90 \times 90}{45 \times 45} \\ &= 2 \times 2 \times 90 \\ &= 360 \end{aligned}$$

6. Solution

Since $120 \times N = 2 \times 2 \times 2 \times 3 \times 5 \times N$ and each prime factor of a perfect square must occur an even number of times, the smallest integer N so that $120 \times N$ will be a perfect square is $2 \times 3 \times 5 = 30$.

7. Solution

Since $28 = 2^2 \times 7$ and $12n = 2^2 \times 3 \times n$, the smallest integer n which will make $12n$ divisible by 28 is 7.

8 Solution

Since $12\,345\,679 \times 9 = 111\,111\,111$, then $12\,345\,679 \times 9 \times 6 = 666\,666\,666$.
Thus, $n = 9 \times 6 = 54$.

9. Solution

The smallest positive integer that is divisible by each of 2, 3, 4, 5, and 6 is 60.
Thus, 61 will leave a remainder of 1 when divided by 2, 3, 4, 5, or 6.
Erin's age is 61.

10. Solution 1

The number of minutes until the two buses leave at the same time is the least common multiple of 45 and 54.
Since $45 = 9 \times 5$ and $54 = 9 \times 6$, the L.C.M. is $9 \times 5 \times 6 = 270$.
Since 270 minutes is 4 hours, 30 minutes, the buses will leave together again at 1830 hours.

Solution 2

The uptown bus leaves the terminal at 1400, 1445, 1530, 1615, 1700, 1745, and 1830 hours.
The downtown bus leaves the terminal at 1400, 1454, 1548, 1642, 1736, and 1830 hours.
Thus, they leave together at 1830 hours.

11. Solution 1

The number of minutes until they sound together again is the least common multiple of 42 and 36.
Since $42 = 2 \times 3 \times 7$ and $36 = 2 \times 2 \times 3 \times 3$, the L.C.M. of 42 and 36 is $2 \times 2 \times 3 \times 3 \times 7 = 252$.
Thus, they will sound together after 252 minutes, or 4 hours and 12 minutes.
Therefore, they will sound together at 1:12 p.m.

Solution 2

The bell sounds at 9:00, 9:42, 10:24, 11:06, 11:48, 12:30, 1:12, 1:54, ...
The buzzer sounds at 9:00, 9:36, 10:12, 10:48, 11:24, 12:00, 12:36, 1:12, 1:48, ...
They sound together at 1:12 p.m.

12. Solution

The large gear makes $\frac{20}{32} = \frac{5}{8}$ of a revolution for each revolution of the small gear.
When the small gear has made 36 revolutions, the large gear has made $\frac{5}{8} \times 36 = 22.5$ revolutions.

13. Solution

$$\begin{aligned} 265\ 265 &= 265\ 000 + 265 \\ &= 265(1000 + 1) \\ &= 265(1001) \end{aligned}$$

In general,
$$\begin{aligned} abc\ abc &= abc000 + abc \\ &= abc(1000 + 1) \\ &= abc(1001) \end{aligned}$$

Therefore, 1001 is always the largest divisor since *abc* is only a three-digit number.

14. Solution

Since *bcd* is divisible by 5, $d = 5$.
Since *cde* is divisible by 3, $c + d + e$ is divisible by 3.
The only possibilities for *cde* are 153, 351, 354, and 453.
But *abc* is divisible by 4.
Therefore, $c = 4$ and so *cde* is 453.
Then *abc* is 214 or 124.
But 214 is not divisible by 4.
Hence, the number is 12453.

Number Sentences and Word Problems

Multiple Choice Questions

1. Solution
   The family has two parents, two daughters, and six sons, or a total of 10 people.
   The answer is D.

2. Solution
   If 6 is one-third of a number, the number is 18.
   Then twice the number is 36.
   The answer is E.

3. Solution
   Since $\frac{3}{5}$ of the number of cookies is 15, the total number of cookies baked was 25.
   The number of cookies left for Dale was 10.
   The answer is E.

4. Solution 1
   The original number is $2(39 - 15) = 48$.

   Solution 2
   Let the original number be x.
   $$\frac{1}{2}x + 15 = 39$$
   $$\frac{1}{2}x = 24$$
   $$x = 48$$
   Therefore, the original number is 48.
   The answer is C.

5. Solution
   $$\frac{1}{2}N + 7 = 21$$
   $$\frac{1}{2}N = 14$$
   $$N = 28$$
   The answer is B.

6. Solution

$x + 5 = 26 + 4x$

$x = 21 + 4x$

$-3x = 21$

$x = -7$

The answer is B.

7. Solution 1

Since $\frac{8}{14} = \frac{4}{7}$, the equation is $\frac{4}{7} \times n = \frac{4}{7}$.

Hence, the value of n is 1.

Solution 2

Multiply both sides of the equation by $\frac{7}{4}$.

$\frac{7}{4}\left(\frac{4}{7} \times n\right) = \frac{7}{4} \times \frac{8}{14}$

$n = 1$

The answer is D.

8. Solution

If $x + 2y = 3$, then $2y = 3 - x$.

Divide both sides of this equation by 2 to give $y = \frac{3-x}{2}$.

The answer is B.

9. Solution

The car averages $144 \div 12 = 12$ km/L.

Thus, the car would require $336 \div 12 = 28$ L of gas for a 336 km trip.

The answer is B.

10. Solution

A selling price of 12¢ a dozen is equivalent to 1¢ per egg.

Therefore, the cost of 151 eggs was 151 cents.

The answer is D.

11. Solution

Twice the original number is $42 - 4 = 38$.

Thus, the original number is 19.

If she had first added 4 and then doubled, the answer would have been $2(19 + 4) = 46$.

The answer is E.

12. Solution

    It takes Nancy $8 \times 12 = 96$ hours to paint a house.
    If she works 6 hours a day, it would take her $96 \div 6 = 16$ days to paint the same house.
    The answer is B.

13. Solution

    Suppose that Ann has n dollars.
    Then Joe has $(n + 15)$ dollars and Henry has $(n + 39)$ dollars.

$$\begin{aligned} n + (n + 15) + (n + 39) &= 99 \\ 3n + 54 &= 99 \\ 3n &= 45 \\ n &= 15 \end{aligned}$$

    Therefore, Ann has 15 dollars.
    The answer is A.

14. Solution

    Since the price is an exact number of dollars, the number of gloves sold must be a divisor of 473.
    The divisors of 473 are 1, 11, 43, and 473.
    These are all possible answers, but the only one given is 11.
    The answer is C.

15. Solution

    Wonder Woman runs at 5 km per minute or 1 km in 12 seconds.
    Superman runs at 3 km per minute or 1 km in 20 seconds.
    Since Wonder Woman gives Superman a five-second head start, she will win by 3 seconds.
    The answer is A.

Full Solution Questions

1. Solution

    The weight of the diamond is $969.1 \times 0.2 = 193.82$ grams.

2. Solution 1

    We can find the original number by working backwards from the answer.
    The number is $(88 - 8) \div 8 = 10$.

Solution 2

Let the original number be x.

$$\begin{aligned} 8x + 8 &= 88 \\ 8x &= 80 \\ x &= 10 \end{aligned}$$

The original number is 10.

3. Solution

If twice a number is 36, the number is 18.

Three times the number is $3 \times 18 = 54$.

4. Solution

Let the number be n.

$$\begin{aligned} 3n - 2 &= 2n + 8 \\ n &= 10 \end{aligned}$$

The number is 10.

5. Solution

Since 3 pounds of sugar cost \$2.85, 1 pound of sugar costs \$0.95.

Therefore, 7 pounds of sugar cost $7 \times 0.95 = \$6.65$.

6. Solution

The gentleman's bill was $2 \times 0.75 + 0.30 + 0.25 = \$2.05$.

His change from \$5.00 was $5.00 - 2.05 = \$2.95$.

7. Solution

$$\begin{aligned} 4a - 3b &= 2a + 5b \\ 2a &= 8b \\ a &= 4b \end{aligned}$$

Therefore, $b:a = 1:4$.

8. Solution 1

Since $a - 1$, a, and $a + 1$ are three consecutive integers whose sum is 27, the middle integer is $27 \div 3 = 9$.

Thus, the value of a is 9.

Solution 2

$$\begin{aligned} (a-1) + a + (a+1) &= 27 \\ 3a &= 27 \\ a &= 9 \end{aligned}$$

The value of a is 9.

9. Solution 1

Since the ratio 3:5 is equivalent to the ratio 15:25, and since $15 + 25 = 40$, the larger number is 25.

Solution 2

Let the two numbers be $3n$ and $5n$.

$$3n + 5n = 40$$
$$8n = 40$$
$$n = 5$$

The larger number is $5n = 25$.

10. Solution

From the first two statements we can deduce that a big burger costs $4.40 - 2.90 = \$1.50$.

From the third statement we know that a soft drink costs $2.10 - 1.50 = \$0.60$.

Thus, an order of fries costs $4.40 - 2(1.50) - 0.60 = \$0.80$.

Therefore, Eddie's order will cost him $3(1.50) + 2(0.80) + 0.60 = \$6.70$.

11. Solution

From one meeting to the next, Kit and Sandy together cover the complete distance around the track.

Since they meet after 20 seconds, Kit has run $\frac{20}{60} = \frac{1}{3}$ of the distance around the track.

Thus, Sandy runs $\frac{2}{3}$ of the distance in 20 seconds.

Therefore, it will take $\frac{3}{2} \times 20 = 30$ seconds for Sandy to run around the track.

12. Solution

The entire amount of ingredients in the mixture is $\frac{1}{2} + \frac{1}{2} + \frac{1}{2} + 3 = \frac{9}{2}$ cups.

The ratio of the maple syrup to the entire mixture is $\frac{1}{2} : \frac{9}{2} = 1:9$.

13. Solution

Let the number of students be n.

Then the cost per student is $\frac{300}{n}$ cents.

If two students have no money, the cost for each of the remaining $(n - 2)$ students is $\frac{300}{n-2}$ cents.

Since the difference between these costs is 40 cents per student, then

$$\frac{300}{n-2} - \frac{300}{n} = 40.$$

By trying $n = 3, 4,$ and 5 we find that $\frac{300}{5-2} - \frac{300}{5} = 100 - 60 = 40$.

Thus, there were 5 students originally involved.

14. Solution 1

To form the three sums, each of the three positive numbers is used twice.
Thus, $180 + 208 + 222 = 610$ represents twice the sum of the three numbers.
Hence, the sum of the three numbers is 305.
The sum of the two smaller numbers is 180.
Thus, the greatest of the three positive integers is $305 - 180 = 125$.

Solution 2

Let the three integers, in increasing order, be x, y, and z.
Then, $x + y = 180$
$x + z = 208$
$y + z = 222$
Adding the three equations gives
$2x + 2y + 2z = 610$
$x + y + z = 305$
But $x + y = 180$.
Hence, $180 + z = 305$
$z = 305 - 180$
$= 125$
The greatest of the integers is 125.

15. Solution

$(1 + 3 + 5 + 7 + \cdots + 119 + 121) - (2 + 4 + 6 + 8 + \cdots + 118 + 120)$
$= 1 + (3 - 2) + (5 - 4) + (7 - 6) + \cdots + (119 - 118) + (121 - 120)$
$= 1 + 1 + 1 + 1 + \cdots + 1 + 1$ (61 terms)
$= 61$
The difference is 61.

Counting and Logic - II

Multiple Choice Questions

1. Solution
   The word MATHEMATICS requires 11 spaces.
   The remaining 26 spaces must be evenly divided at the beginning and at the end.
   Hence, $\frac{26}{2} = 13$ blank spaces must be left before typing the M.
   The answer is C.

2. Solution
   The distance from J to L is $93 - 18 = 75$.
   The distance from J to K is $\frac{2}{3} \times 75 = 50$.
   The number located at K is $18 + 50 = 68$.
   The answer is D.

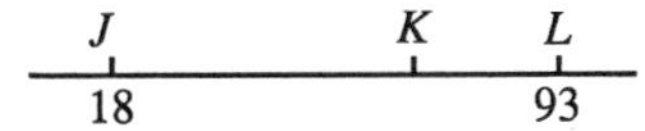

3. Solution
   Since the quotient of p and q is -1, p and q are equal in magnitude but opposite in sign.
   Hence, their sum is zero.
   The answer is E.

4. Solution
   If Lorie is one-third of the way up the stairs and she climbs to one-half of the way up, she climbs $\frac{1}{2} - \frac{1}{3} = \frac{1}{6}$ of the way.
   Since $\frac{1}{6}$ of the way is 11 steps, the number of steps in the flight of stairs is
   $6 \times 11 = 66$.
   The answer is B.

5. Solution
   The number of people who ate both hot dogs and hamburgers was 10.
   The number of people who ate only hot dogs was $15 - 10 = 5$.
   The number of people who ate only hamburgers was $12 - 10 = 2$.
   The number of people who ate neither was 3.
   The number of people at the party was
   $10 + 5 + 2 + 3 = 20$.
   This result is illustrated in the Venn diagram at the right.
   The answer is A.

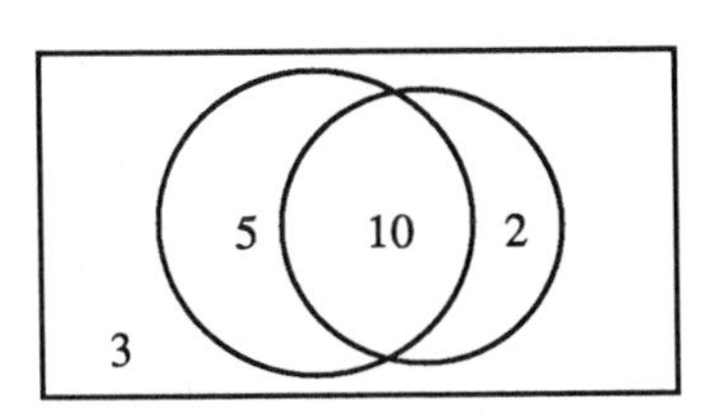

6. Solution 1

In order to determine an approximation to the product, we consider

$6\,000\,000 \times 50\,000 = 300\,000\,000\,000$.

We conclude that the product is a twelve digit number.

Since the product of the units digit is 36, the final digit of the answer is 6.

Of the answers given, the one that satisfies these two conditions is 306 218 475 956.

Solution 2

As in Solution 1, we conclude the product is a twelve digit number.

For those using calculators, the product begins with 306.

The correct product is 306 218 475 956.

The answer is D.

7. Solution

If $y = -2$, then $2y = 2(-2) = -4$

$$-\frac{2}{y} = \frac{-2}{-2} = 1$$

$$\frac{3}{4}y = \frac{3}{4}(-2) = -\frac{3}{2}$$

$$-y^2 = -(-2)^2 = -4$$

$$\frac{1}{8}y^2 = \frac{1}{8}(-2)^2 = \frac{1}{2}$$

Since the largest of these numbers is 1, then $-\frac{2}{y}$ is the greatest.

The answer is B.

8. Solution

To correct the error, the student could take the two steps of subtracting 35 095 and adding 35.95.

The single entry having this effect is $-35\,095 + 35.95 = -35\,059.05$.

The student should subtract 35 059.05.

The answer is B.

9. Solution

To find k, p, q, and r, we add 1588 and $k359$ to obtain the sum $6pqr$.

$$\begin{array}{cccc} 1 & 5 & 8 & 8 \\ k & 3 & 5 & 9 \\ \hline 6 & 9 & 4 & 7 \end{array}$$

Hence, $k = 5$, $p = 9$, $q = 4$, and $r = 7$.

The answer is B.

10. Solution

Since $\frac{a}{b} = \frac{c}{d}$, then $ad = bc$.

Answers (A) and (C) both give this result.

Since $ad = bc$, then $a^2d^2 = b^2c^2$, so (B) is correct.

Consider $\frac{a+b}{b} = \frac{c+d}{d}$.

$$ad + bd = bc + bd$$

$$ad = bc$$

Thus, (E) is true.

But, $\frac{a}{d} \neq \frac{b}{c}$ if $c \neq d$.

For example, $\frac{2}{5} = \frac{6}{15}$, but $\frac{2}{15} \neq \frac{5}{6}$.

The answer is D.

11. Solution

If the sum of the digits of a number is 3, then the number is divisible by 3.

Hence, there are no prime numbers with digits that have a sum of 3, except 3 itself.

The numbers less than ten thousand with digits that have a sum of 2 are 1100, 1010, 1001, 110, 101, 11, and 2.

The only even prime number is 2, so the even numbers 1100, 1010, and 110 are not prime.

Since $1001 = 7 \times 11 \times 13$, it is not prime.

Thus, the only prime numbers less than ten thousand with digits that have a sum of 2 or 3 are 2, 3, 11, and 101.

The number of such primes is 4.

The answer is A.

12. Solution

Since each of the three trees contains at least four Blue Jays and two Orioles, twelve Blue Jays and six Orioles have perched, leaving three Blue Jays and eight Orioles.

To produce the greatest number in a tree, as many as possible of the remaining birds should be put in one particular tree.

If the three remaining Blue Jays are put in one tree, the number of Blue Jays in that tree is now seven.

Since no tree may hold more Orioles than Blue Jays, five of the remaining Orioles may perch here.

The number of birds in the tree is fourteen.

The remaining Orioles may be placed in the remaining trees.

The maximum number of birds in one tree is fourteen.

The answer is A.

Full Solution Questions

1. Solution

   From the beginning of a blast until the beginning of the next blast is a period of 10 seconds.

   In $3\frac{1}{2}$ hours, there are $\frac{7}{2} \times 60 \times 60 = 12\,600$ seconds.

   Therefore, the number of blasts is $12\,600 \div 10 = 1260$

2. Solution 1

   After eight games, eight teams are unbeaten.

   After four more games, four teams are unbeaten.

   After two more games, two teams are unbeaten.

   After one more game, a champion is declared.

   The total number of games required is $8 + 4 + 2 + 1 = 15$.

   Solution 2

   Since there are 16 teams, one will emerge as champion and 15 teams will each lose one game.

   Thus, 15 games are required to determine the champion.

3. Solution

   Three 8-slice pizzas contain 24 slices.

   Since each of the five students eats the same number of slices, the total number of slices eaten could be 5, 10, 15, or 20.

   The number of slices that could be left over is 19, 14, 9, or 4.

4. Solution

   In the nineteen hundreds, the only palindromic number is 1991.

   In the twenty hundreds, the number is 2002.

   In the twenty one hundreds, the number is 2112.

5. Solution

   To achieve a score of 21 using the fewest number of darts, score as many 5s as possible, and then as many 3s as possible.

   This is accomplished by throwing three 5s and two 3s, a total of 5 darts.

6. Solution 1

The numbers are 579
597
759
795
957
975

The sum is 4662.

Solution 2

Each column consists of two 5s, two 7s, and two 9s.

Hence, the sum of each column is $2 \times 5 + 2 \times 7 + 2 \times 9 = 42$.

Therefore, the sum is $42 + 42(10) + 42(100) = 42 + 420 + 4200 = 4662$.

7. Solution

The factors of any perfect square must occur in pairs.

Since $24 = 2 \times 2 \times 2 \times 3$, we must multiply by an additional 2 and an additional 3 to produce a perfect square.

Thus, the least positive integer by which 24 could be multiplied to give a perfect square is $2 \times 3 = 6$.

8. Solution

Since there are five students who played both in the band and volleyball, the number of students who played in either one or both activities was $12 + 17 - 5 = 24$.

The number of students in the class who did not participate in either of these two activities was $30 - 24 = 6$.

This result is illustrated in the Venn diagram at the right.

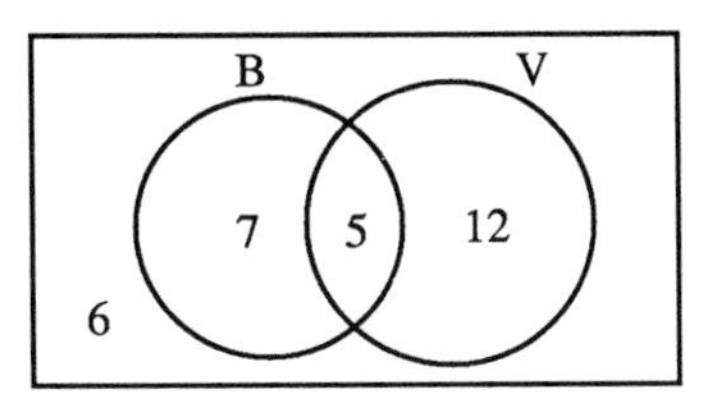

9. Solution

To obtain the least value of $\frac{y}{x}$, we need the smallest value of y combined with the largest value of x.

Thus, the least value of $\frac{y}{x}$ is $\frac{20}{8} = \frac{5}{2}$.

To obtain the greatest value of $\frac{y}{x}$, we need the largest value of y combined with the smallest value of x.

Thus, the greatest value of $\frac{y}{x}$ is $\frac{40}{4} = 10$.

10. Solution

Since Joe has lost four games, he must play and win four games to break even, plus five more games to have \$1.25 more than at the beginning.
Thus, the least number of games that must have been played is $4 + 4 + 5 = 13$.

11. Solution 1

If each person had a picture taken with 11 others, there would be a total of
$12 \times 11 = 132$ pictures.
But this is counting each pair of people twice.
Thus, the minimum number of pictures that could be taken is $132 \div 2 = 66$.

Solution 2

The first person will have his picture taken with 11 others.
The second person will now have his picture taken with ten other individuals.
Similarly, the third person will now have his picture taken with nine other individuals.
The second last person will have his picture taken with the last person.
Therefore, the number of pictures is $11 + 10 + 9 + 8 + ... + 3 + 2 + 1 = 66$.

12. Solution

If a December contains five Sundays, the final Sunday must be on one of December 29, 30, or 31.
Then, the corresponding first Sundays in the month must occur on December 1, 2, or 3.
These patterns are illustrated below.

Sun	Mon	Tues	Wed	Sun	Mon	Tues	Sun	Mon
1				2			3	
8				9			10	
15				16			17	
22	23	24	25	23	24	25	24	25
29				30			31	

Thus, December 25 may occur on a Monday, Tuesday, or Wednesday.

13. Solution

To maximize the number of cages, place as few pigeons as possible in each of the cages.
Since every cage used must house at least one pigeon and no two cages may contain the same number of pigeons, place 1 pigeon in the first cage, 2 pigeons in the second cage, 3 pigeons in the third cage, and so on.
By continuing this pattern up to 13, the number of pigeons accounted for is
$1 + 2 + 3 + 4 + 5 + 6 + 7 + 8 + 9 + 10 + 11 + 12 + 13 = 91$.

The nine remaining pigeons cannot be placed in a fourteenth cage since that would result in two cages having the same number of pigeons.
The nine remaining pigeons must be distributed within the thirteen cages used to this point.
This assignment can be done in many ways, one such being to place all 9 in the thirteenth cage.
Another way would be to have 14, 13, 12, 11, 10, 9, 8, 7, 6, 4, 3, 2, 1 pigeons in the cages.
In any case, the maximum number of cages that can be used to house the 100 pigeons is 13.

2-Dimensional Geometry - II

Multiple Choice Questions

1. Solution

Since the sum of the angles of a quadrilateral is $360°$, $\angle BCD = 360° - 80° - 98° - 106°$

$= 76°$

The answer is C.

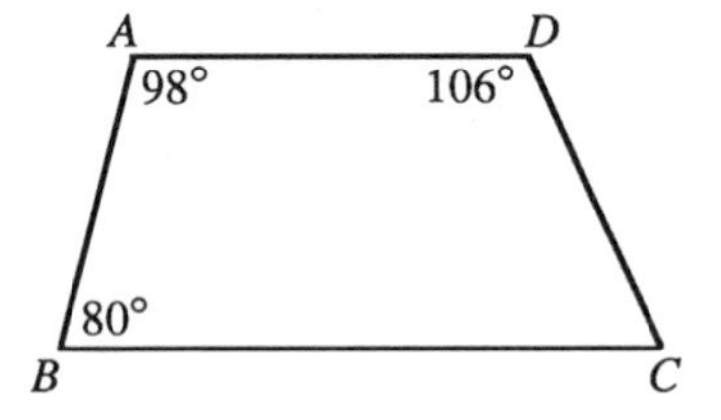

2. Solution

Let $\angle C = x°$ and $\angle A = 2x°$.

Then, $2x + x + 66 = 180$

$3x = 114$

$x = 38$

The smallest angle is $38°$.

The answer is C.

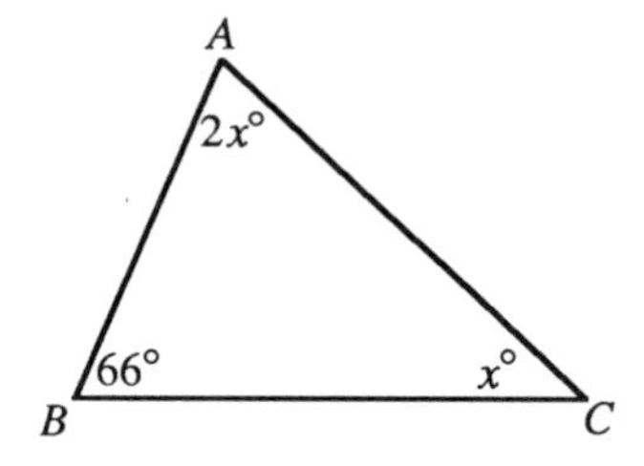

3. Solution 1

Since ADC is a straight angle,

$\angle ADB + \angle BDC = 180°$.

$\angle ADB = 180° - 119°$

$= 61°$

Therefore, $\angle ABD = 180° - 62° - 61°$

$= 57°$

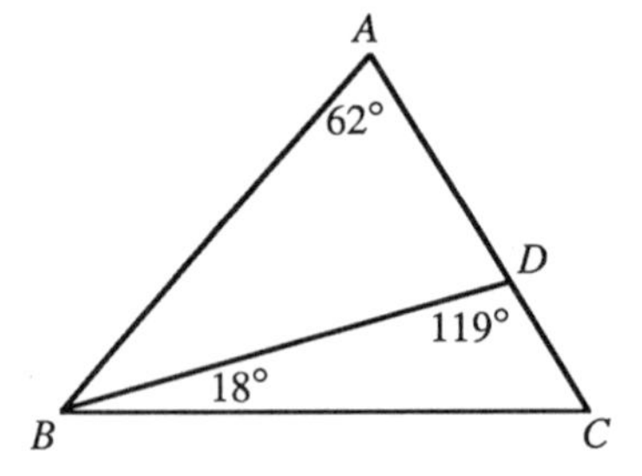

Solution 2

In ΔBDC, $\angle C = 180° - 119° - 18° = 43°$.

Therefore, $\angle ABC = 180° - 43° - 62° = 75°$.

Hence, $\angle ABD = 75° - 18° = 57°$.

The answer is B.

4. Solution

Since $\angle BOC$ and $\angle FOE$ are opposite angles,
$\angle BOC = 30°$.
$\angle AOB + \angle BOC + \angle COD = 180°$
$110° + 30° + y° = 180°$
Hence, $y = 40$.
The answer is E.

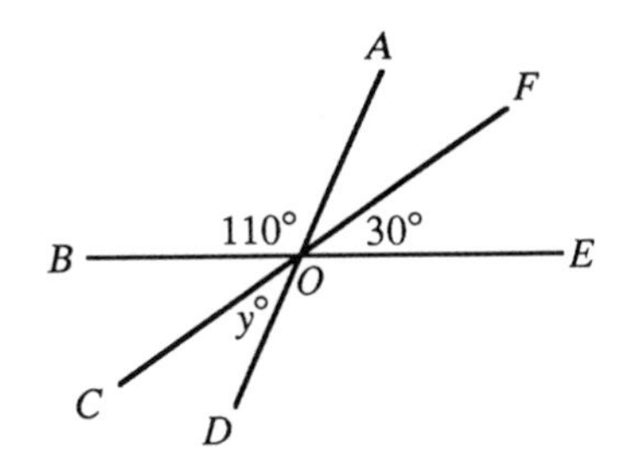

5. Solution

Since the sum of the lengths of any two segments is greater than the length of the third segment, a triangle can be formed.
Since $4^2 + 5^2 \neq 6^2$, the triangle is not right-angled.
Since no two sides are equal in length, the triangle is scalene.
The answer is C.

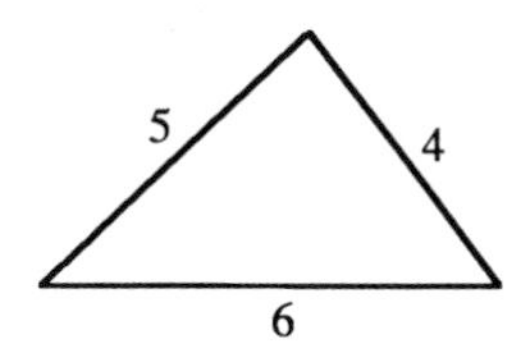

6. Solution

Diagram (A) represents a vertical slide or translation of the triangle.
Diagram (B) represents a reflection of the triangle in the y-axis.
Diagram (C) represents a horizontal translation of the triangle.
Diagram (E) represents a reflection of the triangle in the origin.
Diagram (D) represents a reflection of the triangle in the x-axis.
The answer is D.

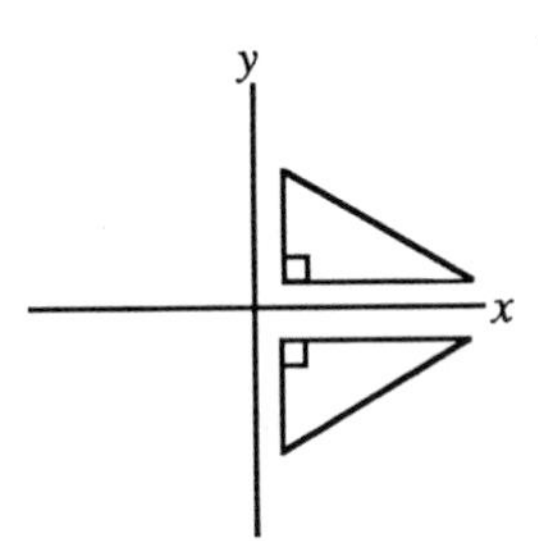

7. Solution

A line of symmetry of a figure divides the figure into two parts such that each is a mirror image of the other.
For the given figure, there are six lines of symmetry, as shown in the diagram.
The answer is C.

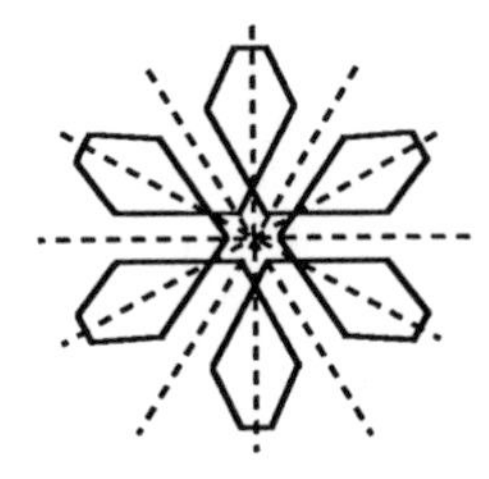

8. Solution 1

The fraction that \$15 is of \$120 is $\frac{15}{120} = \frac{1}{8}$.

In order that the sector be proportional to the amounts distributed, $x = \frac{1}{8} \times 360° = 45°$.

Solution 2

Since \$120 is distributed over 360°, each dollar is represented by 3°.

Thus, \$15 requires a sector angle of $15 \times 3° = 45°$.

The answer is D.

9. Solution

Since the sum of the lengths of any two sides of a triangle must be greater than the length of the third side, the third side cannot have length 2.

The answer is A.

10. Solution

The radius of the circle is 9 cm.

The area of the circle is $\pi(9)^2 = 81\pi$ cm^2.

The area of the four shaded sectors is

$$\left(\frac{4}{6} \times 81\pi\right) = 54\pi$$
$$\approx 54 \times 3$$
$$= 162 \text{ cm}^2$$

Of the answers given, the best approximation is 200 cm^2.

The answer is A.

11. Solution

The distance of the sailboat from the dock, D, is represented by AD.

By the Pythagorean Theorem,

$$(AD)^2 = (AB)^2 + (BD)^2$$
$$= 81 + 144$$
$$= 225$$

Therefore, $AD = \sqrt{225} = 15$.

The sailboat is 15 km from the dock.

The answer is B.

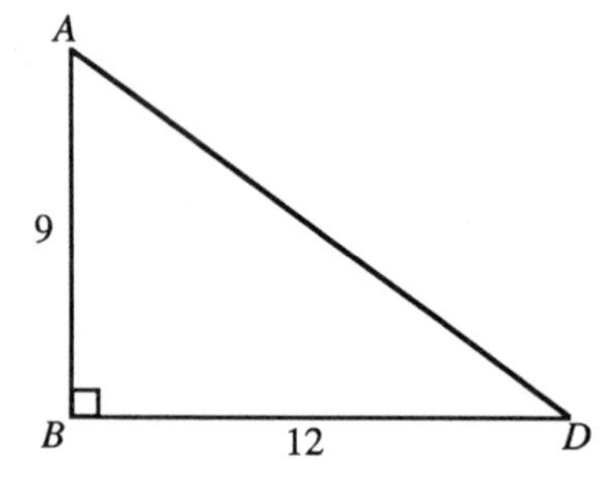

12. Solution

Let the height of the tower be h m.

Since the shadows are 0.8 m and 4 m,

$$\frac{h}{4} = \frac{1.8}{0.8}$$

$$h = \frac{(4)(1.8)}{0.8} = 9$$

The height of the tower is 9 m.

The answer is C.

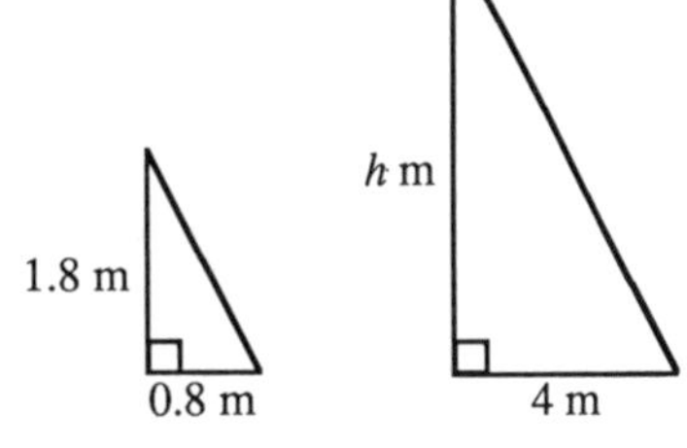

13. Solution

By the Pythagorean Theorem, $(AB)^2 = (BC)^2 + (AC)^2$.

$$\begin{aligned} \text{Therefore, } BC &= \sqrt{(AB)^2 - (AC)^2} \\ &= \sqrt{26^2 - 24^2} \\ &= \sqrt{676 - 576} \\ &= \sqrt{100} \\ &= 10 \end{aligned}$$

The foot of the ladder is 10 m from the base of the wall.

The answer is D.

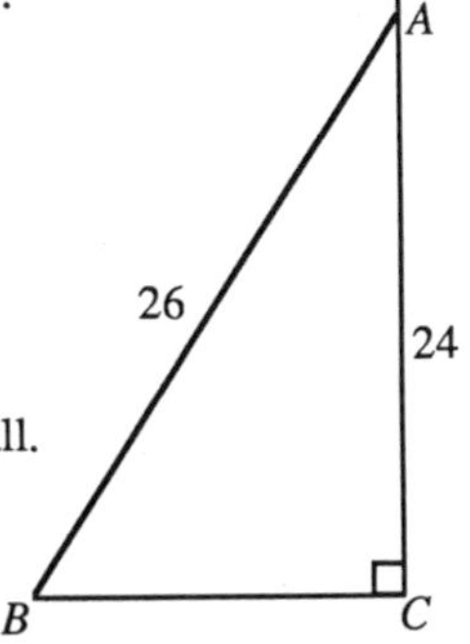

14. Solution

In the line through 4, 5, and 6, the image of 2 is 8, the image of 9 is 3, and the image of 4 is 4. Therefore, the vertices of the reflected triangle are 3, 4, and 8.

The answer is A.

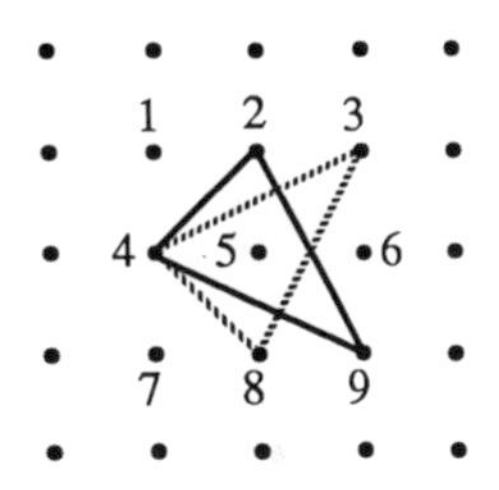

15. Solution

Let the length of the rectangle be x cm and the width be w cm.

Since the perimeter of the rectangle is 40 cm, $x + w = 20$.

The following table displays some possible values for the dimensions and areas of rectangles satisfying the given conditions.

x	0	1	2	5	10	15	18	19	20
w	20	19	18	15	10	5	2	1	0
Area	0	19	36	75	100	75	36	19	0

From the table, we observe that as x takes on values from 0 cm to 20 cm, the area increases from 0 cm^2 to a maximum value of 100 cm^2, and then decreases to 0 cm^2.
We also note the values for the area are symmetric about the value 100. The correct graph is shown.
The answer is D.

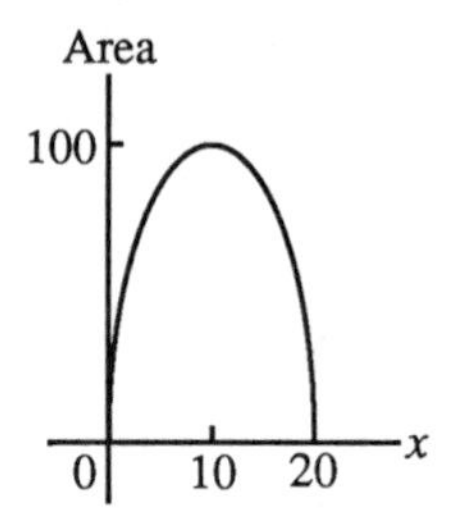

Full Solution Questions

1. Solution

Let angle C be x degrees.
Then, angle B is $5x$ degrees.

$$\angle B + \angle C = 180° - \angle A$$
$$5x + x = 180° - 120°$$
$$6x = 60°$$
$$x = 10°$$

Therefore, angle C is 10°.

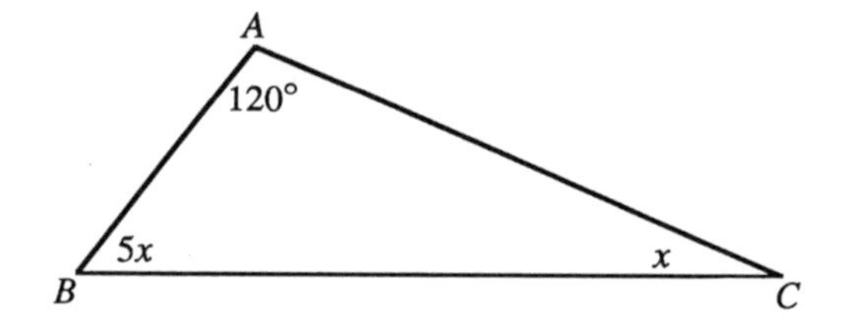

2. Solution

Since the angles are in the ratio 2:5:11, we can let them be $2x$, $5x$, and $11x$ degrees, respectively.

Then, $2x + 5x + 11x = 180°$
$$18x = 180°$$
$$x = 10°$$

The smallest angle is $2x$ or 20 degrees.

3. Solution

Since angles PRQ and PRS form a straight angle, $\angle PRS = 180° - 120° = 60°$.
Similarly, $\angle PSR = 180° - 110° = 70°$.
In ΔPRS, the sum of the three interior angles is 180°.
Thus, $\angle RPS + 60° + 70° = 180°$.
Hence, $\angle RPS = 180° - 130° = 50°$.

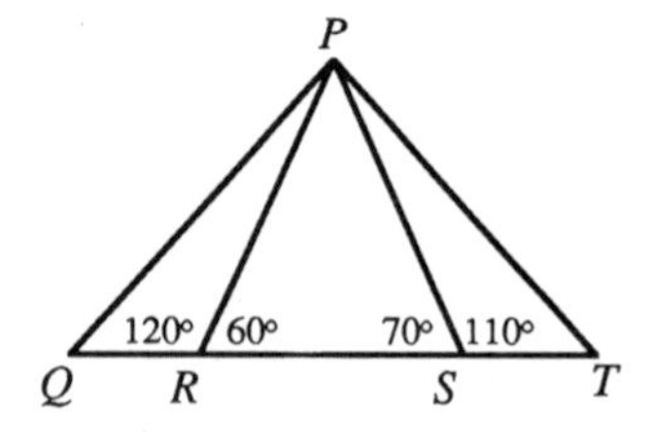

4. Solution

Since $AD = DB$, ΔADB is isosceles and so
$\angle DAB = \angle DBA = 40°$.
Therefore, $\angle ADB = 180° - 40° - 40° = 100°$.
Since ADC is a straight angle,
$\angle BDC = 180° - 100° = 80°$.
Since ΔBDC is isosceles, $\angle BDC = \angle BCD = 80°$.
Therefore, $\angle DBC = 180° - 80° - 80° = 20°$.

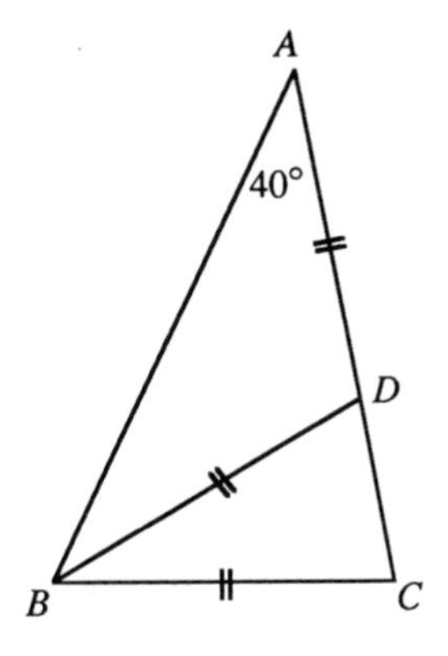

5. Solution

Since $\angle ABC = 90°$, by the Pythagorean Theorem,

$$AC = \sqrt{15^2 + 8^2} = \sqrt{289} = 17$$

Similarly, in ΔDBC,

$$DC = \sqrt{6^2 + 8^2} = \sqrt{100} = 10$$

The perimeter of ΔADC is $9 + 10 + 17 = 36$ cm.

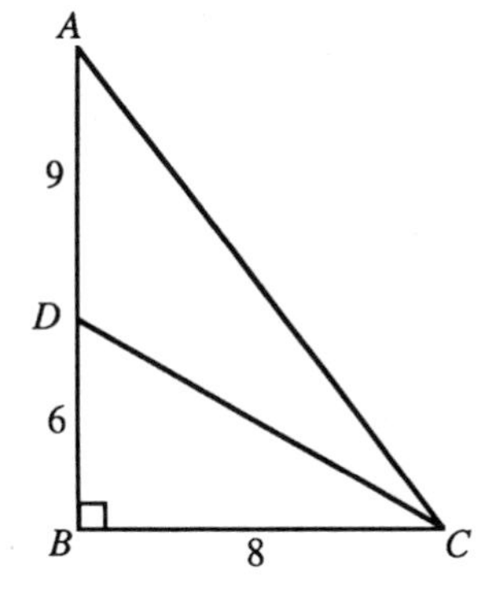

6. Solution

The dotted lines divide the rectangle into four equal rectangles.
Each shaded triangle is one-half of one of these rectangles.
Thus, the two shaded parts are $\frac{1}{4}$ of the original rectangle.

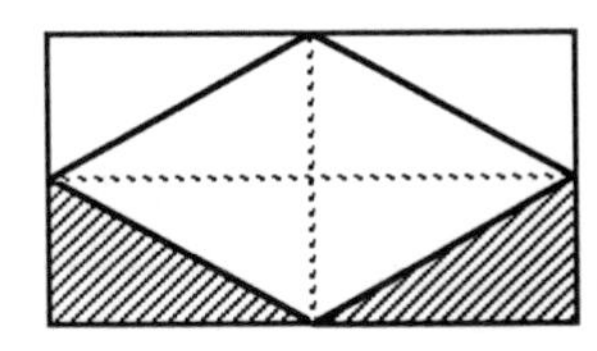

7. Solution

The tiles can be arranged to form a rectangle in two ways

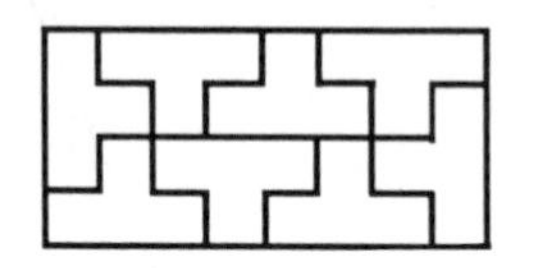

OR

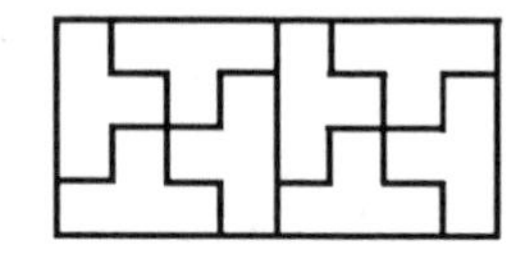

In either case, 8 tiles are required.

8. Solution

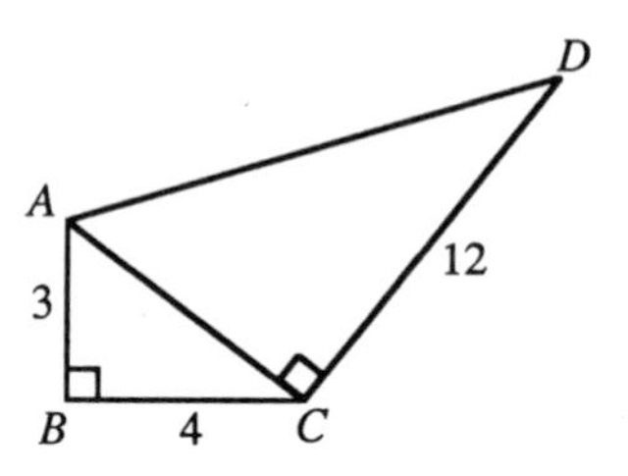

By the Pythagorean Theorem, $(AC)^2 = (AB)^2 + (BC)^2$
$= 9 + 16$
$= 25$

Similarly, in triangle ACD, $(AD)^2 = (AC)^2 + (DC)^2$
$= 25 + 144$
$= 169$

Therefore, the length of AD is $\sqrt{169} = 13$.

9. Solution

The length of AB is $0.5 - 0.1 = 0.4$.
The length of AC is $1.0 - 0.1 = 0.9$.
The fraction that 0.4 is of 0.9 is $\frac{0.4}{0.9} = \frac{4}{9}$.
Thus, AB is $\frac{4}{9}$ of AC.

10. Solution

In one hour, the minute hand of a clock sweeps out an angle of 360°.
Therefore, in each minute the hand sweeps out an angle of $360° \div 60 = 6°$.
From 8:15 a.m. to 8:40 a.m. is a total of 25 minutes, so the hand sweeps out $6 \times 25 = 150°$.

11. Solution

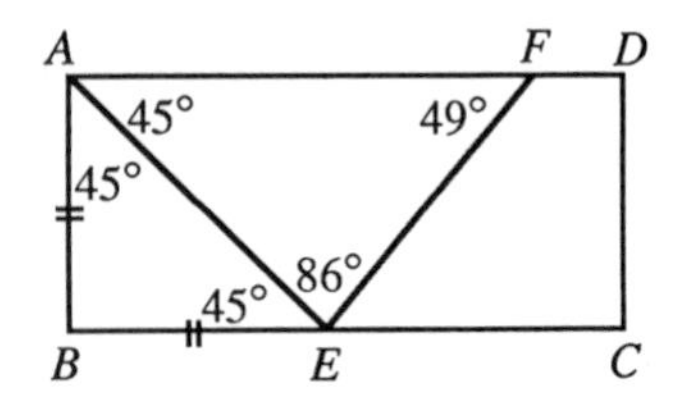

Since $BA = BE$, ΔABE is an isosceles right-angled triangle.
Therefore, $\angle EAB = \angle AEB = 45°$.
Thus, $\angle EAF = 90° - 45° = 45°$.
Therefore, in ΔAEF,

$\angle AFE = 180° - \angle EAF - \angle AEF$
$= 180° - 45° - 86°$
$= 49°$

12. Solution

Let $\angle S = x°$.

Then, $\angle Q = 4x°$.

Since the sum of the angles in a quadrilateral is 360°, $x + 90 + 4x + 120 = 360$

$$5x + 210 = 360$$
$$5x = 150$$
$$x = 30$$

The number of degrees in angle S is 30.

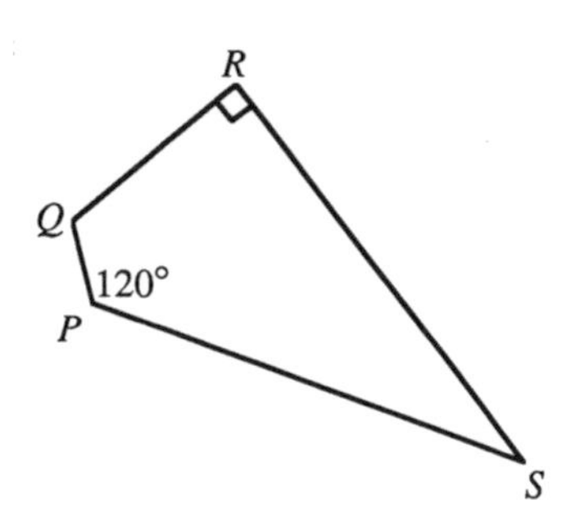

13. Solution 1

The ratio of the actual height of the metre stick to its length in the photograph is $100{:}2 = 50{:}1$.

Therefore, the actual height of the brick wall is $50 \times 4.5 = 225$ cm.

Solution 2

The ratio of the height of the metre-stick to the height of the brick wall in the photograph is $2{:}4.5 = 1{:}2.25$.

Therefore, the wall is 2.25 times as high as the metre-stick.

Since the metre-stick is actually 100 cm high, the brick wall must actually be $100 \times 2.25 = 225$ cm high.

14. Solution

To use the least number of tiles, the size of the tiles must be as large as possible. Since the tiles are square and must completely cover the rectangle, the length of the side of the tile must be a factor of both 70 and 84.

The highest common factor of 70 and 84 is 14.

Thus, each tile is 14 cm by 14 cm and a total of $5 \times 6 = 30$ tiles will be required.

Number Patterns and Sequences - II

Multiple Choice Questions

1. Solution

$1 + 3 + 5 + 7 + 9 + 11 = 36$

$= 6^2$

The answer is A.

2. Solution 1

The sequence is 7, 20, 33, 46, 59, 72, 85, ...
Hence, 72 is counted.

Solution 2

Let the number of 13s that are added to 7 be n.
Then, $7 + 13n$ must be a number in the seventies.
Thus, $n = 5$ and $7 + 13n = 7 + 65 = 72$.
The answer is C.

3. Solution

$2^2 - 1^2 = 3$

$4^2 - 3^2 = 7$

$6^2 - 5^2 = 11$

$8^2 - 7^2 = 15$

$10^2 - 9^2 = 19$

Add: $10^2 - 9^2 + 8^2 - 7^2 + 6^2 - 5^2 + 4^2 - 3^2 + 2^2 - 1^2 = 19 + 15 + 11 + 7 + 3$

$= 55$

The answer is E.

4. Solution 1

$1 + 2 + 3 + 4 + 5 + 6 + 7 + 8 + 9 + 10 + 9 + 8 + 7 + 6 + 5 + 4 + 3 + 2 + 1$

$= (1 + 9) + (2 + 8) + (3 + 7) + (4 + 6) + (5 + 5) + (6 + 4) + (7 + 3) + (8 + 2) + (9 + 1) + 10$

$= 10 \times 10$

$= 100$

Solution 2
$1 + 2 + 3 + 4 + 5 + 6 + 7 + 8 + 9 + 10 + 9 + 8 + 7 + 6 + 5 + 4 + 3 + 2 + 1$
$= 2(1 + 2 + 3 + 4 + 5 + 6 + 7 + 8 + 9) + 10$
$= (2 \times 45) + 10$
$= 90 + 10$
$= 100$
The answer is C.

5. Solution
When $n = 1$, $n^2 - 4n = 1 - 4 = -3$.
When $n = 2$, $n^2 - 4n = 4 - 8 = -4$.
When $n = 3$, $n^2 - 4n = 9 - 12 = -3$.
The product is $(-3)(-4)(-3) = -36$.
The answer is B.

6. Solution
Since there are $420 - 20 = 400$ students who are not on the team, the ratio of basketball players to non-basketball players is 20:400.
The answer is D.

7. Solution
Each of the fractions results in a repeating decimal with the repeating part the same as the numerator of the fraction.
Using this pattern, $0.41144114 = \frac{4114}{9999}$.
The answer is C.

8. Solution
There are five equal spaces between points M and R.
Since M and R are 15 units apart, the adjacent letters represent points that are 3 units apart.
Hence, the number at Q is 12.
The answer is C.

9. Solution
If the square root of the number is between 6 and 7, the number is between 36 and 49.
Since $3^3 = 27$ and $4^3 = 64$, the cube root of the number is between 3 and 4.
The answer is C.

10. Solution

    Since there were 50 000 mites one hour ago, the number of mites now present is
    $50\,000 \times 2 \times 2 = 200\,000$.
    If the mites were placed end to end in a line, the length of this line would be
    $200\,000 \times 0.00002 = 4$ cm.
    The answer is E.

11. Solution

    The differences between successive pairs of integers in the sequence are 1, 3, 5, 7, ...
    If this pattern continues, the sequence is 1, 2, 5, 10, 17, 26, 37, 50, ...
    The seventh number is 37.
    The answer is C.

12. Solution

    The number of seconds in a year is $365 \times 24 \times 60 \times 60 \approx 31\,500\,000$.
    We note that $2^{25} \approx 33\,500\,000$.
    Thus, the largest interval within a year between snaps is 2^{24} seconds.
    The number of times Pat would snap his fingers in a year, including the initial snap, would be 25.
    The answer is B.

Full Solution Questions

1. Solution

    The sum of the first 30 natural numbers is
    $$\frac{30(30+1)}{2} = \frac{30 \times 31}{2} = 15 \times 31 = 465$$

2. Solution

    The total amount he had given me was $1 + 2 + 4 + 8 + 16 + 32 + 64 + 128 = 255$ dollars.

3. Solution 1

    The weekly heights of the first plant form the sequence 12, 14, 16, 18, 20, ...
    The weekly heights of the second plant form the sequence 3, 8, 13, 18, 23, ...
    They reach the same height, 18 cm, in 3 weeks.

Solution 2

Let the number of weeks before they are the same height be n.

When they are the same height, $12 + 2n = 3 + 5n$

$$3n = 9$$

$$n = 3$$

Therefore, they reach the same height in 3 weeks.

4. Solution 1

$1 + 3 + 5 + 7 + \ldots + 93 + 95 + 97 + 99$

$= (1 + 99) + (3 + 97) + (5 + 95) + \ldots + (49 + 51)$

$= 100 + 100 + 100 + \ldots + 100$ (50 terms)

$= 25 \times 100$

$= 2500$

The sum of the odd integers from 1 to 99 inclusive is 2500.

Solution 2

Consider the partial sums:

$S_1 = 1 = 1^2$

$S_2 = 1 + 3 = 4 = 2^2$

$S_3 = 1 + 3 + 5 = 9 = 3^2$

$S_4 = 1 + 3 + 5 + 7 = 16 = 4^2$

In general, the sum of the first n positive odd integers is n^2.

Therefore, the sum of the first 50 positive odd integers is $50^2 = 2500$.

5. Solution

Since all the years between 1900 and 1999 start with the digits 1 and 9, which have sum 10, the years whose digits have a sum of 20 will be those in which the last two digits have a sum of 10.

The pairs of single digit numbers that have a sum of 10 are 1 and 9, 2 and 8, 3 and 7, 4 and 6, and 5 and 5.

Each of these pairs, except the 5 and 5, gives two years (e.g., 1919 and 1991) while the 5 and 5 gives only the year 1955.

There are 9 years between 1900 and 1999 whose digits have a sum of 20.

6. Solution 1

The ratio 7:5:1 is equivalent to the ratio 350:250:50.

Hence, there are a total of 350 + 250 + 50 = 650 girls, boys, and teachers in the school.

Solution 2

Let the number of girls in the school be G and the number of boys be B.

Then, $\frac{G}{7} = \frac{B}{5} = \frac{50}{1}$.

Therefore, $G = 350$ and $B = 250$.

The total number of girls, boys, and teachers in the school is $350 + 250 + 50 = 650$.

Solution 3

The ratio 7:5:1 means that for every one teacher in the school there are seven girls and five boys.

Therefore, for every one teacher there are actually $7 + 5 + 1 = 13$ people in the school.

Since there are 50 teachers, there are $50 \times 13 = 650$ girls, boys, and teachers in the school.

7. Solution

The largest denomination that can be used is 10¢.

The combinations possible, using only the numbers 1, 5, and 10, that add to 18, are:

$10 + 5 + 1 + 1 + 1$

$10 + 1 + 1 + 1 + 1 + 1 + 1 + 1 + 1$

$5 + 5 + 5 + 1 + 1 + 1$

$5 + 5 + 1 + 1 + 1 + 1 + 1 + 1 + 1 + 1$

$5 + 1 + 1 + 1 + 1 + 1 + 1 + 1 + 1 + 1 + 1 + 1 + 1 + 1$

$1 + 1 + 1 + 1 + 1 + 1 + 1 + 1 + 1 + 1 + 1 + 1 + 1 + 1 + 1 + 1 + 1 + 1$

Thus, there are six ways that 18¢ can be made from these coins.

8. Solution

The two-digit whole numbers are 10, 11, 12, ..., 99.

Each of the integers 1, 2, 3, ..., 9 appears as a tens digit exactly 10 times.

Therefore, the sum of the digits in the tens place is $10(1 + 2 + 3 + 4 + ... + 9)$

$$= 10 \times 45$$
$$= 450$$

9. Solution 1

The palindromic numbers between 100 and 200 are 101, 111, 121, 131, 141, 151, 161, 171, 181, and 191.

Therefore, $a = 10$.

The palindromic numbers between 1000 and 2000 are 1001, 1111, 1221, 1331, 1441, 1551, 1661, 1771, 1881, and 1991.

Therefore, $b = 10$.

Hence, $b - a = 10 - 10 = 0$.

Solution 2

Palindromes between 100 and 200 are of the form 1■1 where ■ $\in$ {0, 1, 2, ..., 9}.
Similarly, palindromes between 1000 and 2000 are of the form 1■■1 where
■ $\in$ {0, 1, 2, ..., 9}.
Therefore, the number of palindromes in each interval is the same, and so $b - a = 0$.

10. Solution 1

Let n represent the number of kilometres travelled on the first day.
The number of kilometres travelled during the five days is given by the sequence
$n, n + 15, n + 30, n + 45, n + 60$.

$$\begin{aligned} \text{Thus, } n + (n + 15) + (n + 30) + (n + 45) + (n + 60) &= 410 \\ 5n + 150 &= 410 \\ 5n &= 260 \\ n &= 52 \end{aligned}$$

The distance travelled on the first day was 52 kilometres.

Solution 2

The average distance travelled each day was $410 \div 5 = 82$ km.
Hence, on the third day, a distance of 82 km was travelled.
Thus, on the first day, a distance of $82 - 15 - 15 = 52$ km was travelled.

11. Solution

After planting 5 primroses, there were four spaces to plant 4 primroses.
Then there were eight spaces to plant 8 peonies.
This created sixteen spaces to plant petunias and these, in turn, created thirty-two more spaces to plant pansies.
The total number of plants in the row was $5 + 4 + 8 + 16 + 32 = 65$.

12. Solution

In the integers from 1 to 89 inclusive, the digit 9 occurs nine times.
From 90 to 99 there are 11 nines.
Thus, there are 20 nines from 1 to 99.
Similarly, between 1 and 99 inclusive, there are 20 of each of the digits 1, 2, 3, ..., 8.
The sum of all the digits of the numbers from 1 to 99 is

$$\begin{aligned} &20 \times 1 + 20 \times 2 + 20 \times 3 + \ldots + 20 \times 9 \\ &= 20(1 + 2 + 3 + 4 + 5 + 6 + 7 + 8 + 9) \\ &= 20 \times 45 \\ &= 900 \end{aligned}$$

Since the sum of the digits in 100 is 1, the sum of all the digits of the numbers from 1 to 100 inclusive is 901.

13. Solution 1

$1 + 2 - 3 + 4 + 5 - 6 + 7 + 8 - 9 + ... + 22 + 23 - 24 + 25$
$= (1 + 2 - 3) + (4 + 5 - 6) + (7 + 8 - 9) + ... + (22 + 23 - 24) + 25$
$= 0 + 3 + 6 + ... + 21 + 25$
$= 3(1 + 2 + 3 + ... + 7) + 25$
$= 3(28) + 25$
$= 109$

Therefore, the sum of the first 25 terms is 109.

Solution 2

$1 + 2 - 3 + 4 + 5 - 6 + 7 + 8 - 9 + ... + 22 + 23 - 24 + 25$
$= (1 + 2 + 3 + 4 + 5 + 6 + ... + 25) - 2(3 + 6 + 9 + ... + 24)$
$= (1 + 2 + 3 + 4 + 5 + 6 + ... + 25) - 6(1 + 2 + 3 + ... + 8)$
$= \frac{25 \times 26}{2} - \frac{6 \times 8 \times 9}{2}$
$= 325 - 216$
$= 109$

Therefore, the sum of the first 25 terms is 109.

3-Dimensional Geometry - II

Multiple Choice Questions

1. Solution

Let the height of the box be h cm.
The volume, V, of the box is
$V = \text{length} \times \text{width} \times \text{height}$.
Thus, $6 \times 6 \times h = 72$.
The height of the box is 2 cm.
The answer is B.

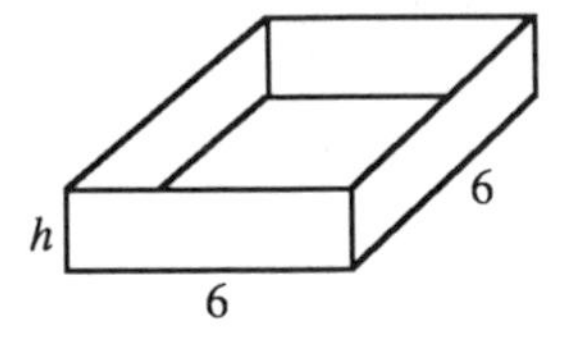

2. Solution 1

Let the third dimension of the rectangular box be h m.
Thus, $6 < h < 10$.
Hence, the volume of the box is a value between $6 \times 6 \times 10$ m^3 and $6 \times 10 \times 10$ m^3, i.e., between 360 m^3 and 600 m^3.
Of the values given, the only volume the box could have is 480 m^3.

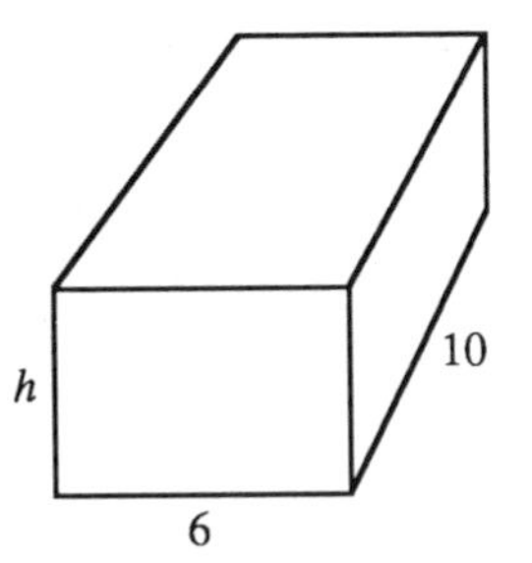

Solution 2

Let the third dimension of the rectangular box be h m.
Thus, $6 < h < 10$.
The volume of the box is $V = 6 \times 10 \times h$
$= 60h$ m^3
Since $6 < h < 10$, then $360 < V < 600$.
Of the numbers given, the only value that V could have is 480.
The answer is D.

3. Solution 1

Place the cube so the face marked W is on the bottom.
Since faces R and S share a vertex in common with face W, when folded R and S will be adjacent and vertical.
Similarly, since faces R, S, and X share a common vertex, when folded face X will be on the top.

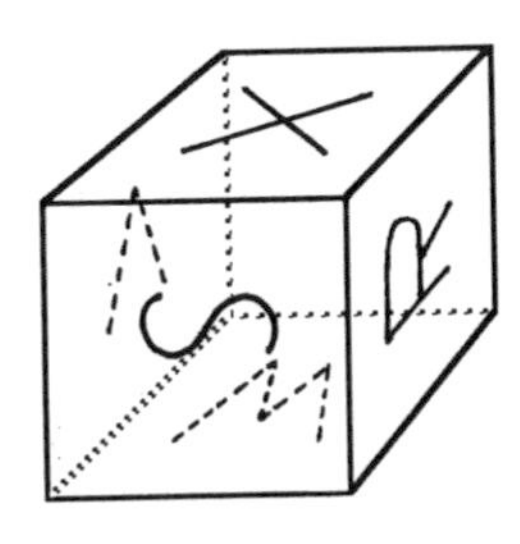

Hence, the letter on the face opposite the face marked W is X.

Solution 2

Opposite faces must not share any common vertices.
Hence, W is opposite X, V, or K.
But S must be opposite K and so R must be opposite V.
It follows that W is opposite X.
The answer is A.

4. Solution 1

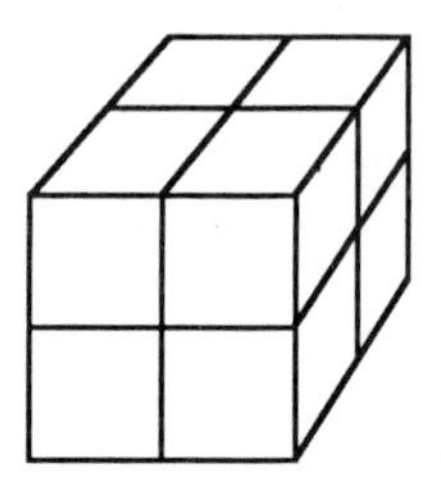

Let each edge of the larger cube have length 2 units.
Thus, each edge of the smaller cube has length 1 unit.
The surface area of the larger cube is $6 \times 2 \times 2 = 24$ square units.
The total surface area of the 8 smaller cubes is $8 \times 6 \times 1 \times 1 = 48$ square units, which is double that of the large cube.

Solution 2

Three of the six faces of the 8 smaller cubes form the surface area of the large cube.
Thus, the total surface area of the 8 smaller cubes is double that of the large cube.

Solution 3

Any cut parallel to the face of a cube creates two new faces equal in area to the original opposite parallel faces.
Thus, after three such cuts, the total surface area is double that of the original cube.
The answer is C.

5. Solution

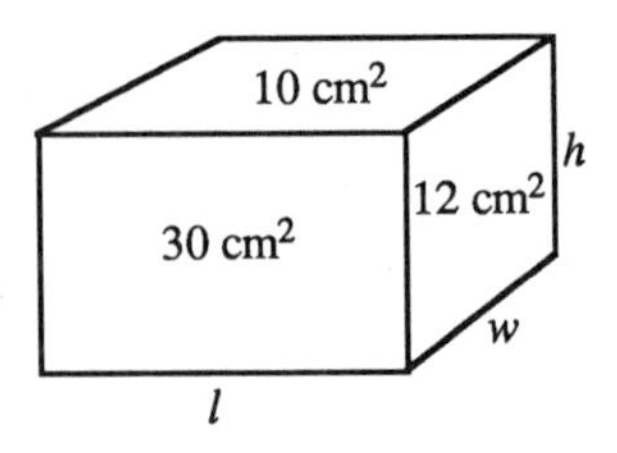

Let the dimensions of the box be l, w, and h, as shown.
The volume of the box is lwh.
We are given that $lh = 30$, $lw = 10$, and $wh = 12$.
Multiplying these three quantities yields

$$(lh)(lw)(wh) = (30)(10)(12)$$
$$l^2w^2h^2 = 3600$$

Thus, $lwh = 60$.

The volume of the box is 60 cm^3.
The answer is A.

6. Solution

If the figure is rotated through 180° in a counterclockwise direction, the figure in (A) is obtained. None of the other figures can be obtained by rotating the given figure. The answer is A.

7. Solution 1

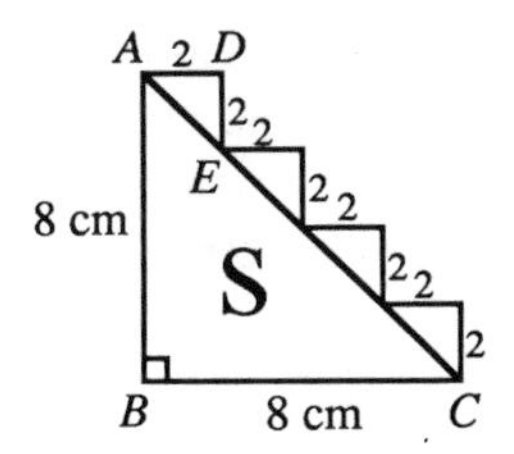

The volume of the solid can be determined by evaluating the product of the area of the face S and the depth of 5.

The height of each of the four steps is 2 cm.

Thus, the width of each of the four steps is 2 cm.

The area of the face S is the sum of the areas of triangle ABC and four times the area of triangle ADE.

$$\begin{aligned}\text{The area of face } S &= \tfrac{1}{2}(8)(8) + 4\left(\tfrac{1}{2}\right)(2)(2) \\ &= 32 + 8 \\ &= 40\end{aligned}$$

The volume of the solid is $40 \times 5 = 200$ cm^3.

Solution 2

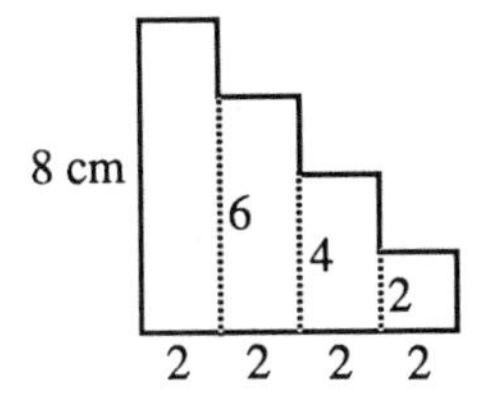

The volume of the solid can be determined by evaluating the product of the area of the face S and the depth of 5 (See solution 1).

Using rectangles, the area of S is equal to

$2 \times 8 + 2 \times 6 + 2 \times 4 + 2 \times 2 = 40$.

The volume of the solid is $40 \times 5 = 200$ cm^3.

Solution 3

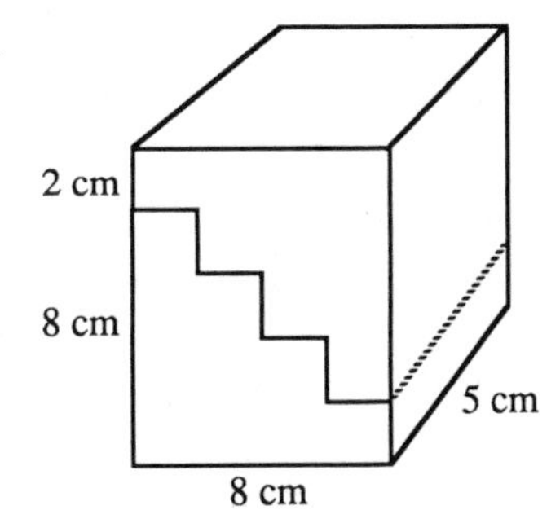

A copy of the solid is turned upside down and "glued" to the original solid.

The volume of the new solid is equal to

$8 \times 10 \times 5 = 400$ cm^3.

The volume of the original solid is 200 cm^3.

The answer is A.

8. Solution

A cube has 8 vertices and 12 edges. Three edges meet at each vertex.
When the fly arrives at any vertex for a second time, the tour is over.
The maximum possible distance the fly could walk would be if it started at a given vertex, walked along the edges so that it arrived at each of the 8 vertices once and then proceeded along an edge to one of the vertices for the second time.
One such path of this type is *ABCDAHGFEH.*
The length of such a tour is 9×10 cm = 90 cm.
The answer is D.

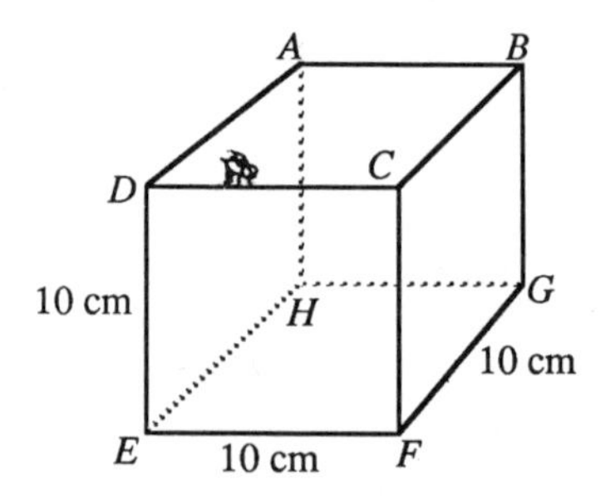

9. Solution

Each vertical side of the object has surface area
$3 \times 3 + 2 \times 2 + 1 \times 1 = 14$.
The surface area of the bottom is $3 \times 3 = 9$.
By projecting the tops of the three cubes on to a flat surface we observe that the total surface area of the tops is equal to that of a 3×3 square, as shown.
Therefore, the total surface area is
$4(14) + 9 + 9 = 74$.
The answer is B.

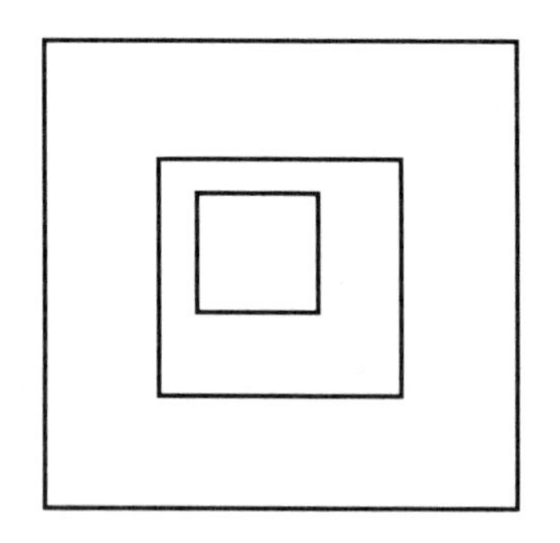

10. Solution

The number of cubes used to build the block is
$3 \times 3 \times 4 = 36$.
There are 18 red cubes and 18 white cubes.
The number of exposed faces is
$(2 \times 3 \times 3) + (2 \times 3 \times 4) + (2 \times 3 \times 4) = 66$, of which 33 are red and 33 are white.
The number of red faces hidden from view equals (the total number of red faces) – (the number of exposed red faces) $= (18 \times 6) - 33$
$= 108 - 33$
$= 75$

The answer is D.

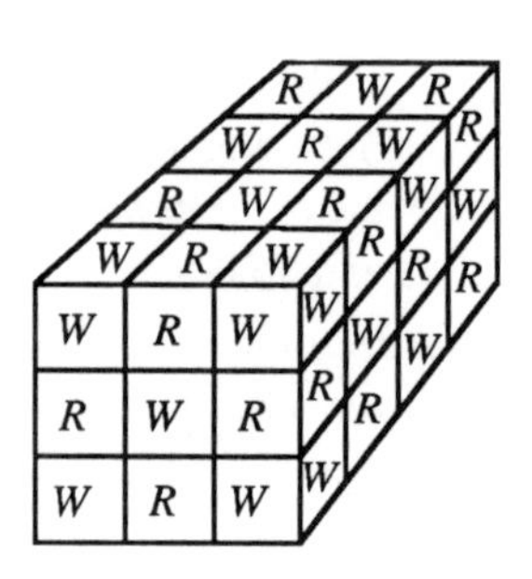

11. Solution

The volume of a cylinder is equal to the area of the base times the height of the cylinder.

The volume of water held by the larger cylinder is $\left[\pi(30)^2\right](h) = 900\pi h$ cm^3.

The volume of water held by each smaller cylinder is $\left[\pi(5)^2\right](h) = 25\pi h$ cm^3.

The number of smaller cylinders required to hold the same volume of water as the large cylinder is $900\pi h \div 25\pi h = 36$.

The answer is D.

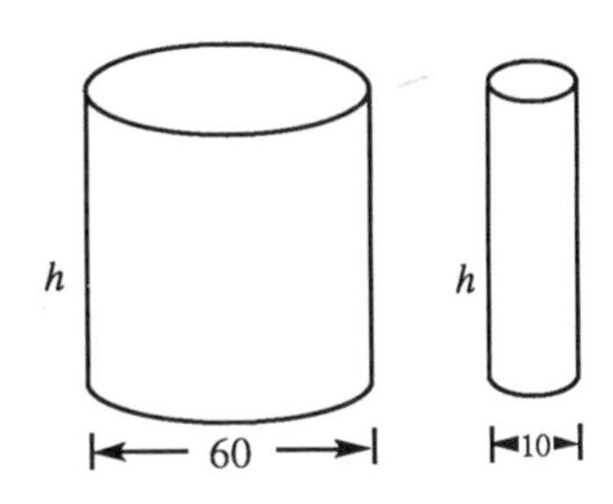

12. Solution

The volume of a prism is equal to cross-sectional area times the length.

Since the length is the same in both positions of the tray, only the cross-sectional areas need be considered.

In the original position, the empty portion has a cross-sectional area of $3 \times 2 = 6$ cm^2.

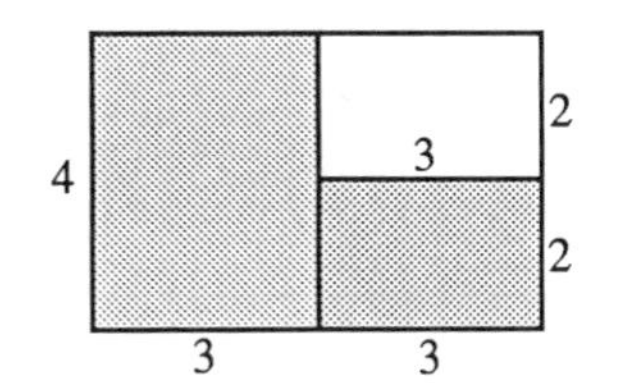

In the tipped position, some of the water from the full section pours into the "half-full" section and some spills out.

Each section will now contain the same volume of water.

The cross-section of the empty portion of each section is a right-angled, isosceles triangle having equal sides of length 3 cm, and area $\frac{1}{2}(3)(3) = \frac{9}{2}$ cm^2.

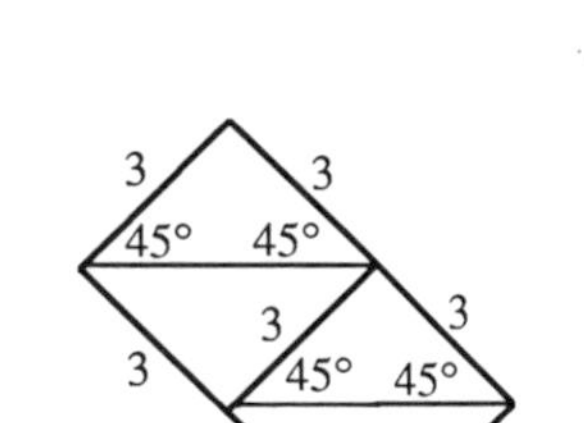

The total cross-sectional area of the empty portions is 9 cm^2, an increase of 3 cm^2 from the original position.

The volume of water that spills out is $3 \times 4 = 12$ cm^3.

The answer is C.

Full Solution Questions

1. Solution
   The total number of blocks used is $9 + 8 + 7 + 6 + 5 + 4 + 3 + 2 + 1 = 45$.

2. Solution 1
   To result in eight identical pieces, a cut must be made half way between each of the pairs of parallel faces of the given block.
   A cube has three such pairs of faces, so three cuts are required.

   Solution 2
   We want to maximize the number of pieces resulting from each cut.
   The greatest number of pieces that can result from a cut is double the original number of pieces.
   Since there is one piece to start with, the first cut results in two pieces, the second cut in four pieces and the third cut in eight pieces.

3. Solution
   Each of the six faces has area $\frac{24}{6} = 4$ cm^2.
   Since each face is a square, each edge of the cube has length 2 cm.
   Thus, the volume of the cube is $2 \times 2 \times 2 = 8$ cm^3.

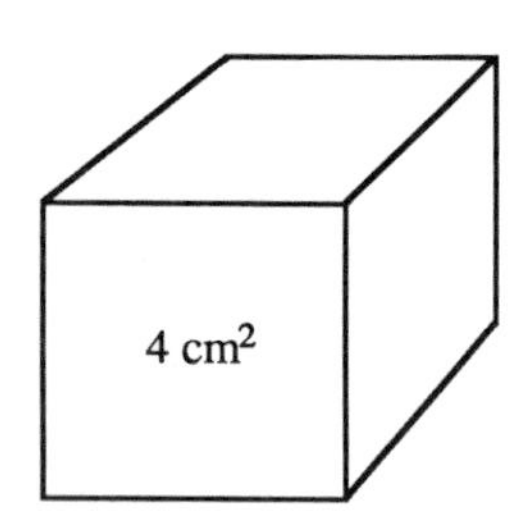

4. Solution
   The T-shaped solid can be thought of as being made from two rectangular blocks.
   Its volume is $(8 \times 5 \times 4) + (2 \times 7 \times 4) = 160 + 56$
   $= 216$ cm^3

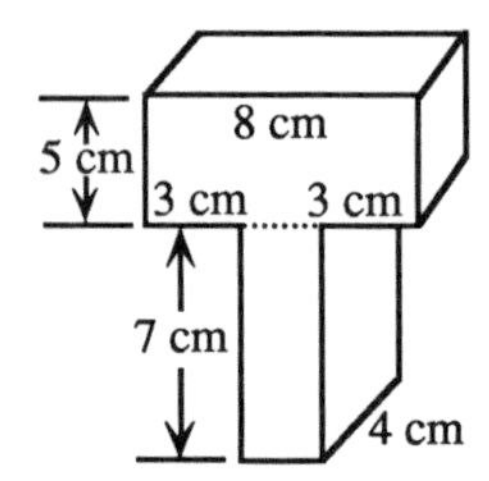

5. Solution

On a die, the numbers on the opposite faces have a sum of 7.
As a result, on die A the numbers on the left and right faces must be 1 and 6.
Since numbers on the touching faces add to 9, the 6 must be on the right face of die A.
We can now proceed to identify the numbers on all remaining faces.
On the left face of B is a 3, on the right face of B is a 4, on the left face of C a 5, on the front face of C a 6, on the back face of D a 3, and finally on the face labelled P is a 4.

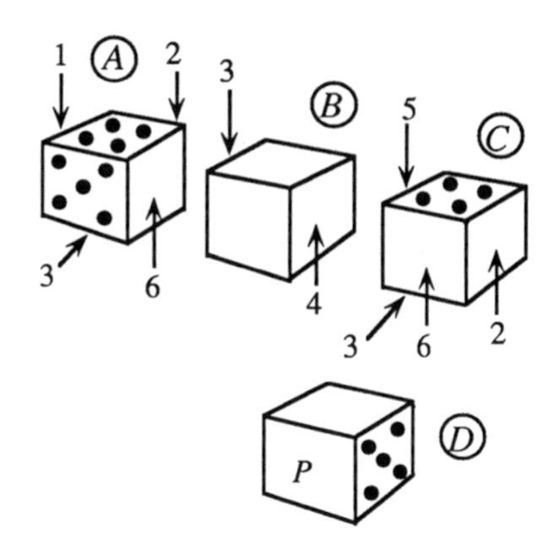

6. Solution

Since the volume of the middle cube is 64 cm^3, its edge length is 4 cm.
Hence, the edge lengths of the five cubes are 16 cm, 8 cm, 4 cm, 2 cm, and 1 cm.
The total volume of the five cubes is $16^3 + 8^3 + 4^3 + 2^3 + 1^3 = 4681$ cm^3.

7. Solution

The volume of the first box is $9 \times 6 \times 24$ cm^3.
If the second box has height h cm, then its volume is $6 \times 4 \times h$ cm^3.

Hence,
$$\begin{aligned} 6 \times 4 \times h &= \tfrac{1}{2}(9 \times 6 \times 24) \\ &= 9 \times 6 \times 12 \\ h &= \frac{9 \times 6 \times 12}{6 \times 4} \\ &= 27 \end{aligned}$$

The height of the second box is 27 cm.

8. Solution

Since the diameter of the cylinder is 5 cm, then its circumference is $\pi(5)$ cm.
The rectangle formed has dimensions 5π cm by 12 cm.
The perimeter of this rectangle is
$12 + 5\pi + 12 + 5\pi = (24 + 10\pi)$ cm.

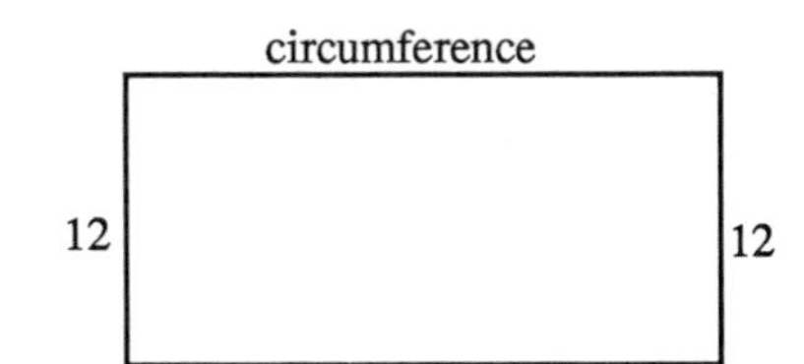

9. Solution

Each cut parallel to a face of the given solid produces two new faces equal in area to the original parallel face.

The new faces will be unpainted.

The horizontal cut parallel to the 5 cm by 5 cm face produces an unpainted surface area of $2 \times (5 \times 5) = 50$ cm^2.

The lengthwise cut parallel to the 4 cm by 5 cm face produces an unpainted surface area of $2 \times (4 \times 5) = 40$ cm^2.

The two crosswise cuts parallel to the 4 cm by 5 cm end faces produces an unpainted surface area of $2 \times [2 \times (4 \times 5)] = 80$ cm^2.

Therefore, the total unpainted surface area of the 12 blocks is 170 cm^2.

10. Solution

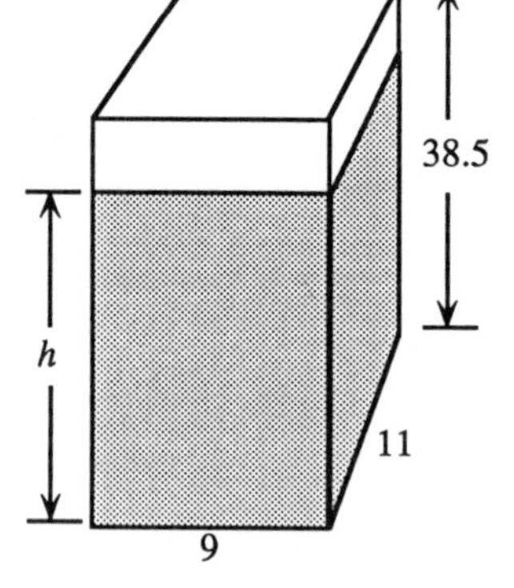

Let the original depth of the water be h cm.

The volume of the water in the container is

$9 \times 11 \times h = 99h$ cm^3.

When the water freezes, the volume expands by 10% resulting in a volume of

$110\% \times 99h = 1.1 \times 99h$ cm^3.

The ice will now completely fill the container so will have a volume of $9 \times 11 \times 38.5$ cm^3.

Thus, $1.1 \times 99h = 9 \times 11 \times 38.5$

$$h = \frac{38.5}{1.1} = 35$$

The container should be filled with water to a depth of 35 cm.

11. Solution

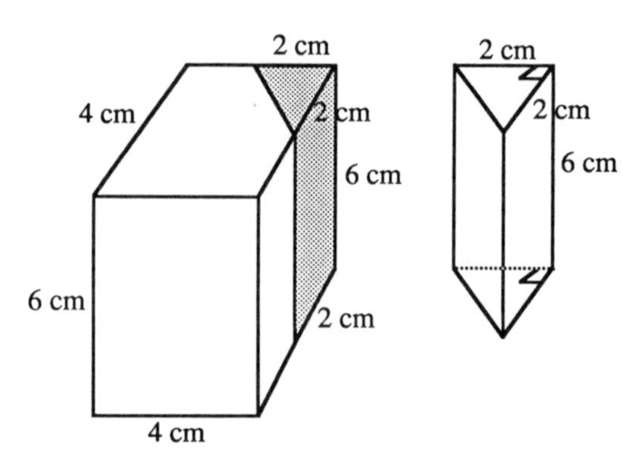

The volume of the original block is $4 \times 4 \times 6 = 96$ cm^3.

The volume of the discarded triangular prism is

(area of base) $\times$ (height)

$= \left(\frac{1}{2} \times 2 \times 2\right) \times (6)$

$= 12$ cm^3

Therefore, the volume of the remaining part of the block is

$96 - 12 = 84$ cm^3.

12. Solution 1

When punching out the designated columns from front to back, 25 of the smaller cubes are removed.

When punching out the designated columns from top to bottom, the number of smaller cubes removed from each level are 5, 2, 0, 2, and 5, respectively.

When punching out the designated columns from side to side, the number of smaller cubes removed from each level are 5, 0, 0, 0, and 5, respectively.

The total number of smaller cubes removed is $25 + 14 + 10 = 49$, leaving $125 - 49 = 76$ cubes.

Solution 2

After all the designated columns have been punched out, the five layers, from front to back, as drawn, illustrate the number of smaller cubes remaining.

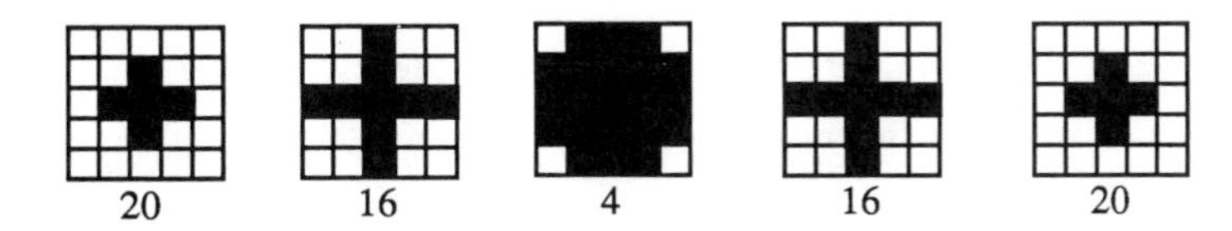

Thus, the total number of smaller cubes remaining is $20 + 16 + 4 + 16 + 20 = 76$.

Miscellaneous and Challenge Problems

Multiple Choice Questions

1. Solution
   On the second day, Mary planted $60 - 38 = 22$ trees.
   Thus, Mary planted 22 trees on the first day.
   The number of trees Bill planted was $38 - 22 = 16$.
   The answer is E.

2. Solution
   $\sqrt{36} - \sqrt{16} = 6 - 4 = 2$
   The answer is A.

3. Solution
   We draw a map showing relative positions of the town.

   The answer is E.

4. Solution
   The train leaves Dunnville at 10:56.
   In two hours, the time will be 12:56.
   Thirty minutes later makes 1:26 the arrival time in Attridgetown.
   The answer is E.

5. Solution
   The largest size is 250 ml and the smallest size is 25 ml.
   Since $250 = 10 \times 25$, the largest size is 10 times the quantity of the smallest size.
   The value of x is 10.
   The answer is C.

6. Solution 1
   Since $72 = 18 \times 4$, $N = 5 \times 4 = 20$.

Solution 2

If $\frac{N}{72} = \frac{5}{18}$, then

$18N = 5 \times 72$ (multiplying both sides by 18 and 72)

$N = \frac{5 \times 72}{18}$

$N = 20$

The answer is A.

7. Solution

In one hour the car travels 90 km which equals 90 000 m.

In one minute the car travels 90 000 m ÷ 60 = 1500 m.

In one second the car travels 1500 m ÷ 60 = 25 m.

In ten seconds the car travels 10 × 25 m = 250 m.

The answer is C.

8. Solution

Janet travels 48 km in 45 minutes.

Hence, Janet travels $\frac{48}{45}$ km in 1 minute and so she travels $\frac{48}{45} \times 60 = 64$ km in one hour.

Therefore, Janet's speed is 64 km per hour.

The answer is C.

9. Solution

The average value of all the door prizes equals

$$\frac{\text{the total value of the prize money}}{\text{the number of prizes}} = \frac{(25)(1) + (20)(2) + (8)(3) + (4)(4) + (3)(5)}{25 + 20 + 8 + 4 + 3}$$

$$= \frac{25 + 40 + 24 + 16 + 15}{60}$$

$$= \frac{120}{60}$$

$$= 2$$

The average value of all the door prizes is $2.00.

The answer is E.

10. Solution

$$1-\cfrac{1}{1-\cfrac{1}{1-\frac{1}{11}}}=1-\cfrac{1}{1-\frac{11}{11-1}}$$

$$=1-\cfrac{1}{1-\frac{11}{10}}$$

$$=1-\frac{10}{10-11}$$

$$=1-\frac{10}{-1}$$

$$=1+10$$

$$=11$$

The answer is A.

11. Solution

The only pairs of positive integers whose sum is 7 are (1, 6), (2, 5), and (3, 4).

The largest possible product is $3 \times 4 = 12$.

The answer is A.

12. Solution

We consider each of the given possibilities.

Since 8 and 9 are not prime, they are rejected.

We now consider 7, 11, and 13.

Since these numbers are all odd, each must be the sum of an even and an odd number.

Since 2 is the only even prime, the only possibilities are

$$7 = 2 + 5$$
$$11 = 2 + 9$$
$$13 = 2 + 11$$

Since 9 is not prime, 11 cannot be written as the sum of two primes.

The answer is D.

13. Solution 1

For all integers greater than 15, the difference between the squares of any two of them is greater than 29.

Considering the squares of the integers from 1 to 15, the only pair whose difference is 29 is $225 = 15^2$ and $196 = 14^2$.

Thus, $m = 15$, $n = 14$, and $mn = 15 \times 14 = 210$, which is between 201 and 250.

Solution 2

The expression $m^2 - n^2 = 29$ may be written as $(m + n)(m - n) = 29 \times 1$.

This is the only way that $m^2 - n^2$ can be factored, and since 29 is prime it can only be factored as 29×1.

Since m and n are positive integers, $m + n$ is greater than $m - n$.

Thus, $m + n = 29$ and $m - n = 1$, which yields $m = 15$ and $n = 14$.

Thus, $mn = 15 \times 14 = 210$.

The answer is D.

14. Solution

Since $63 = 7 \times 9$ and $14 = 7 \times 2$, $63 \div 14 = 4.5$.

We cannot tell whether $31 \div 7$ gives the result without dividing.

However, $44\,285\,714 \div 10 = 4\,428\,571.4$, $40 \div 9 = 4.\dot{4}$ (division by 9 gives a repeating decimal), and since $45 = 5 \times 9$, division by 45 must also give a repeating decimal.

We conclude that $31 \div 7 = 4.4285714$ as a calculator calculation.

The answer is B.

Full Solution Questions

1. Solution

In the first 30 minutes she drives at 60 km/h and travels 30 km.

To complete the trip in one hour she must drive the remaining 50 km in 30 minutes.

Her speed must be 100 km/h.

2. Solution

When $C = -40$, the relation gives

$$\begin{aligned} F &= \tfrac{9}{5}(-40) + 32 \\ F &= 9(-8) + 32 \\ F &= -72 + 32 \\ F &= -40 \end{aligned}$$

The Fahrenheit temperature is -40.

3. Solution

Since the average of the five numbers is 4, their sum is $5 \times 4 = 20$.

Since the average of the four remaining numbers is 2, their sum is $4 \times 2 = 8$.

The number removed is $20 - 8 = 12$.

4. Solution 1

Let the number of problems Gerry found difficult be D.
The number of problems Gerry found easy was $12 - D$.
The difficult problems took, on average, 20 minutes to solve, and the easy problems took, on average, 5 minutes to solve.
She completed the 12 problems in exactly 2 hours, or 120 minutes.

$$\begin{aligned} \text{Thus, } 20(D) + 5(12 - D) &= 120 \\ 20D + 60 - 5D &= 120 \\ 15D &= 60 \\ D &= 4 \end{aligned}$$

Gerry found four of the problems to be difficult.

Solution 2

Each difficult problem required 20 minutes, or 10 minutes more than the average time.
Each easy problem required 5 minutes, or 5 minutes less than the average time.
If Gerry completed the test in the same time (2 hours) then there must have been two easy problems for each difficult one.
Hence, there were four difficult problems.

5. Solution

The total saving to the original five members, was $5 \times \$15.00 = \$75.00$.
Thus, each of the new members contributed $\$75.00 \div 3 = \$25.00$.
Since the total cost was shared equally, the cost of the microcomputer was $8 \times \$25.00 = \$200.00$.

6. Solution

After the president receives his share, the amount of money remaining to be shared is half of the money.
The vice-president gets $\frac{1}{4}$ of $\frac{1}{2}$ or $\frac{1}{8}$ of the earnings.
The amount left to be shared at this point is $\frac{3}{8}$ of the total.
The secretary gets $\frac{1}{3}$ of $\frac{3}{8}$ or $\frac{1}{8}$ of the earnings.
This leaves $\frac{2}{8}$ of the total to be shared equally between the treasurer and you.
Your share of \$3.00 is $\frac{1}{8}$ of the total.
The earnings total $8 \times \$3.00 = \$24.00$.

7. Solution 1

Since the original shape is a square, the resulting figure is also a square.
Since its perimeter is 12 cm, each side has length 3 cm.
The area of the resulting square is 9 cm^2.
The original square has area four times the area of the smaller square.
Its area is $4 \times 9 = 36$ cm^2.

Solution 2

Since the original shape is a square, the resulting figure is also a square.

Since its perimeter is 12 cm, each side has length 3 cm.

Thus, the dimensions of the original square are 6 cm × 6 cm.

The area of the original square is $6 \times 6 = 36$ cm^2.

8. Solution

The vertices in the maze are labelled as indicated in the diagram.

Travelling only east, south, or southeast, the routes from A to B are $ACDEB$, $ACFEB$, $ACFB$, $ACFIB$, $AGFEB$, $AGFB$, $AGFIB$, $AGIB$, and $AGHIB$.

There are 9 routes.

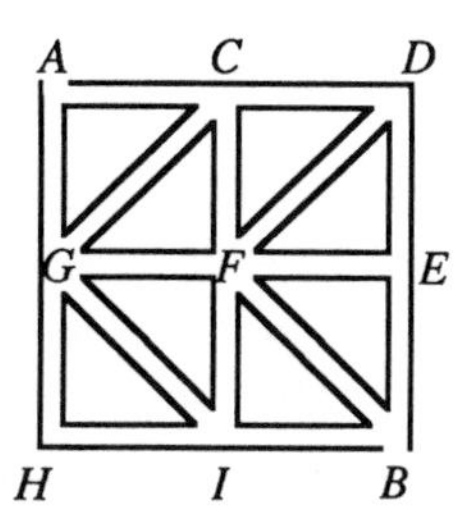

9. Solution 1

By trial, two numbers that have a sum of 8 and a product of 15 are 5 and 3.

Their reciprocals are $\frac{1}{5}$ and $\frac{1}{3}$.

The sum of these reciprocals is $\frac{1}{3} + \frac{1}{5} = \frac{5}{15} + \frac{3}{15}$

$= \frac{8}{15}$

Solution 2

If the numbers are m and n, then $m + n = 8$ and $mn = 15$.

The sum of their reciprocals is $\frac{1}{m} + \frac{1}{n} = \frac{n+m}{mn} = \frac{8}{15}$.

10. Solution

The smallest prime numbers are 2, 3, and 5.

The smallest number to contain these primes is $2 \times 3 \times 5 = 30$.

If the required number is a perfect square, it must contain its factors in pairs.

Hence, the number is $2 \times 2 \times 3 \times 3 \times 5 \times 5 = (30)^2 = 900$.

11. Solution

The relationship $13x + 8y = 1992$ can be thought of as adding x multiples of 13 to y multiples of 8, resulting in the sum of 1992.

$$\underbrace{\overbrace{13 + 13 + 13 + \cdots + 13}^{x \text{ times}} + \overbrace{8 + 8 + \cdots + 8}^{y \text{ times}}}_{(x+y) \text{ times}} = 1992$$

Since 13 is greater than 8, $x + y$ is minimized by using as many 13s and as few 8s as possible.
Dividing 1992 by 13 we obtain $153\frac{3}{13}$.
Hence, $x \leq 153$.
But $x \neq 153$, since $13 \times 153 = 1989$ and no 8's can be used in the total.
However, if $x = 152$, $152 \times 13 = 1976$, and $8y = 16$ to complete the 1992.
Thus, $y = 2$.
The minimum value of $x + y$ is 154.

12. Solution 1
Let the number of horses Old MacDonald has be n.
Hence, he has n cows and n pigs.
The number of troughs required for the horses is $\frac{n}{2}$.
The number of troughs required for the cows is $\frac{n}{3}$.
The number of troughs required for the pigs is $\frac{n}{8}$.
Since there are 69 troughs, $\frac{n}{2} + \frac{n}{3} + \frac{n}{8} = 69$

$$\frac{12n + 8n + 3n}{24} = 69$$
$$23n = 24 \times 69$$
$$n = \frac{24 \times 69}{23}$$
$$= 72$$

The total number of animals is $3 \times n = 3 \times 72 = 216$.

Solution 2
The ratio of the number of troughs required for the cows to the number required for the horses is 2:3.
The ratio of the number of troughs required for the pigs to the number required for the cows is 3:8.
Thus the ratio of the number of troughs required for the pigs to the number required for the cows to the number required for the horses is 3:8:12.
Thus, the total numbers of troughs required for the three types of animals are of the form $3k$, $8k$, and $12k$.
But $3k + 8k + 12k = 69$

$$23k = 69$$
$$k = 3$$

Thus, there are 9 troughs for the pigs, and since there are 8 pigs at each trough there are 72 pigs.
Old MacDonald must also have 72 horses and 72 cows, and the total number of animals is 216.

13. Solution

Hint: Many problems can be successfully approached by listing and counting. Frequently a pattern occurs which allows for a solution.

The integers between 100 and 200, in which the sum of the digits is 10, are 109, 118, 127, 136, 145, 154, 163, 172, 181, and 190.
There are 10 such integers.
The integers between 200 and 300 with this property are 208, 217, 226, 235, 244, 253, 262, 271, and 280.
There are 9 such integers.
Similarly, in the 300s, there occur 307, 316, 325, 334, 343, 352, 361, and 370.
There are 8 such numbers.
Similarly, in the 400s, 500s, ..., 900s there are 7, 6, 5, 4, 3, 2 such integers.
Therefore, the total number of integers between 100 and 1000 such that the sum of the digits is 10, is $10 + 9 + 8 + 7 + 6 + 5 + 4 + 3 + 2 = 54$.

14. Solution

Note: This problem requires that we find what we think is a largest number, and then we justify that this is indeed the largest number which cannot be ordered.

We start by noting that using only multiples of 7 we can place orders for 7, 14, 21, 28, 35, 42, ..., doughnuts.
Using only multiples of 13 we can place orders for 13, 26, 39, 52, ..., doughnuts.
Using only multiples of 25 we can place orders for 25, 50, ..., doughnuts.
Using these and combinations of them, we can place orders for 7, 13, 14, 20(7 + 13), 21, 25, 26, 27, 28, 32, 33, 34, 35, 38(13 + 25), 39, 40(14 + 26), 41(28 + 13), 42, 45(7 + 13 + 25), 46(21 + 25), 47(21 + 26), 48(35 + 13), 49(7 + 42), 50, 51(26 + 25) doughnuts.
We speculate that 44 is the largest order than cannot be placed, but we must justify this.
Note that the orders that can be placed can be related to earlier orders in the sequence; for example, $45 = 7 + 38$, $46 = 7 + 39$, ..., $49 = 7 + 42$.
Adding the 50 and 51 to this set gives seven consecutive acceptable orders.
Thus, an order for 52 is possible by adding 7 to 45, and it now follows that every order that is greater than 45 doughnuts can be placed.
We conclude that 44 is the largest order that cannot be placed.